So now that we've let them have their say, what can [...]
We took Neil and Amanda along to the Rainbow [...]
let the experts loose on them.

Amanda's hair was already streaked blonde, but it looked rather harsh, so Stevin gave her a dark blonde tint to tone it down.

Because she didn't want to lose much length, Stevin cut her hair short at the sides and into the top to take away the bulkiness.

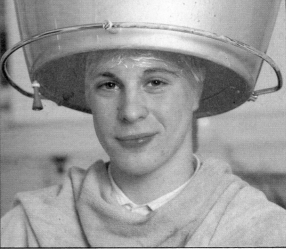

Amanda doesn't usually wear make-up, but she agreed that the look Harriet, our make-up artist, gave her made a difference.

Stevin gave Neil's hair an all-over dark blonde tint to cover the brassy colour, then he added lighter highlights, which looked much more natural.

contents

POP

FEATURES

SHORT STORIES

Printed and published by D. C. Thomson & Co., Ltd., 185 Fleet Street, London EC4A 2HS.
© D. C. Thomson & Co., Ltd., 1986.
ISBN 085116-365-3.

STAR appear

Lazy Libra? Get-up-and-go Gemini? Well, whatever you sign, we have the perfect health and beauty plan for you

The presents have all been opened, the decorations are packed away for another year and (for some strange reason, you can't get your skin fastened) I couldn't be anything to do with the seven empty selection boxes scattered around your bedroom, could it?

But don't worry, because we've enlisted the help of the stars to find a New Year health and beauty plan just for you. So get reading — and get healthy at the same time!

C APRICORN
(Dec. 21-Jan.19)

Capricorns are definitely creatures of habit — and this is where you could have problems. Being settled in your ways doesn't automatically mean that they are healthy ways! What you need to do is establish different habits like a regular healthy diet and some non-strenuous exercise to keep you supple. Once you've got into the new routine, you're in the lucky position of finding it easy to stick to. It's just a question of finding the right habit!

MAKE-UP: Brighten yourself up. Fizzy oranges and vibrant yellows will bring you alive!

A QUARIUS
(Jan. 20-Feb. 18)

There's only one word for you, and that's weird! Aquarians love to be noticed and enjoy doing things that are just that bit different. You're quite figure-conscious and don't usually have to diet as you burn up so much energy just living! If you are overweight, though, cut out those savoury snacks you're so keen on and try an unusual sport like windsurfing.

MAKE-UP: Not too bright, but still different. Use shades of gold and copper with black eyeliner and even black lipstick!

P ISCES
(Feb. 19-March 20)

Dreamy and easy-going, Pisceans don't take failure easily. Because of this, you have to be careful not to set yourself unrealistic targets. If you decide to lose a stone in two weeks, you're obviously going to fail — you'll be discouraged and give up on your diet completely. Slow, steady weight loss is best for you — and stir that lazy Piscean body into some energetic exercise.

MAKE-UP: Dreamy, like you. Pale, romantic shades of blue, soft green and pink for a special occasion.

CANCER (June 21-July 21)

Because you're a water sign, you... are intuitive and sensitive, but you... ignore your own 'hunches' too often. By paying more heed to ... your body gives out, you'll fin... ...cking to a healthy eating and exer... suits your comes very easily to ... support and lifestyle. If lack ...ping you doing encouragement are ... anything, then get a ... to join in with you. And being a water sig... what better exercise than swimming?

MAKE-UP: The mer... d look! Use shades of green, blue and ...aki or soft sea-shell colours.

LIBRA (Sept. 22-Oct. 22)

This is probably the laziest sign of the zodiac and Librans are often overweight. You love a life of luxury and aren't very sporty. Also, if you're feeling bored or depressed, you're likely to turn to food for comfort. Because you love eating, you'd be better to take more exercise than try to really cut down on the calories. Something sociable like dancing would be best.

MAKE-UP: A romantic look suits you best. Shades of pink, lilac and blue will look great!

SCORPIO (Oct. 23-Nov. 21)

You like to collect all the facts before you make a decision, but once committed to something you are thorough and completely dedicated. You want to win at everything you try and, like all the water signs, you have a strong natural sense of timing. When you think things are getting out of control figure-wise, you take drastic measures to sort it out! Learn to use your strong will positively and treat your body with a little more kindness and care. Vigorous exercise presents just the challenge you need to prove how determined you are! Swimming and long-distance running are both right up your street.

MAKE-UP: Dark and dramatic. Go for lots of black and the darker shades...

SAGITTARIUS

ARIES (March 21-April 20)

...appearance, so you probably ...overweight. and especially your ...to take care of your ...diets because you're so impatient. You'll eat ...next to nothing and... very rarely become ...are very strung-... ...unhappy, ...s Ariens ...heir minds to do ...if. they make up ...Crash diets aren't ... good for you, though, ...o try to eat ...sibly, and take up ...exercise ...chase the ...at away.

MAKE-UP: Exciting colours, warm up with ...dramati... black lined eyes, loads of mascara ...and glossy red lips.

TAURUS (April 21-...)

Taureans are ...suspicious people ...they don't consider new... so faddy diets ...tend to ...ar of things ...aren't for you. A straightforward, calorie- ...once you believ... something ...counting diet is best — you know it work... ...you're wrong!). ...change your ... You like to loc... quite a lot of ...so you won't lose faith. Not ...the most ...money doing ...energetic sign of the zodiac, y... or walking ...don't care w... think that you ...are more your line than aerobics — and ...if only tak... ...ment of your new ...watch out for that swe... th your... ...ever wear it again.

MAKE-UP: Keep it subtle. Shades of br... ...min... nd beige will suit you. A pale brow... and natural lipstick complete the ...look.

GEMINI (May 21-June 20)

Geminis want to spa... ...ar whole life enjoying themselves — and that's ...n the ...go, though, and burn... you're always ...calories in everyday life. Because you live ...ast, you like fast food — hamburgers and hot ...dogs are the Gemini's favourites. But fast ...food isn't healthy, so try to get enough rest ...and eat regular meals rather than bingeing ...on junk food. Variety and interest are what ...you need for diet and exercise. Something ...exciting like disco dancing or horse-riding ...would be ideal exercise for you.

MAKE-UP: Someth... br... to match your ...outlook on life. Jazz it up with shades of ...yellow, orange and vivid greens.

LEO (July 22-Aug...)

Proud an... ...strong, you're not ...easily infl... ...by others and ...you bella... ...thing you rarely ...change your m...

...rhythmic stretching ...exercises ...suit you best, along with a ...set diet that g... ...you the challenge you need ...to prove yourse...

MAKE-UP: Drama... Pale skin with shades of ...strong colours—red, black and vibrant reds.

VIRGO (Aug. 22-Sept. 21)

Always on the move, Virgo... are... ...usually overweight. You love order... ...life and hate to waste time, so ea... in your life and... straightforward, repetitive exercise technique like cycling or jogging would suit you and help you maintain a balanced gradual weight loss. You've got a lot of will-power and you're proud of it, but try not to become a diet bore and annoy your friends by giving them a running commentary on the calorie content of everything they eat.

MAKE-UP: Soft shades. Blues and beiges are the colours for you with lips that are pretty in pink.

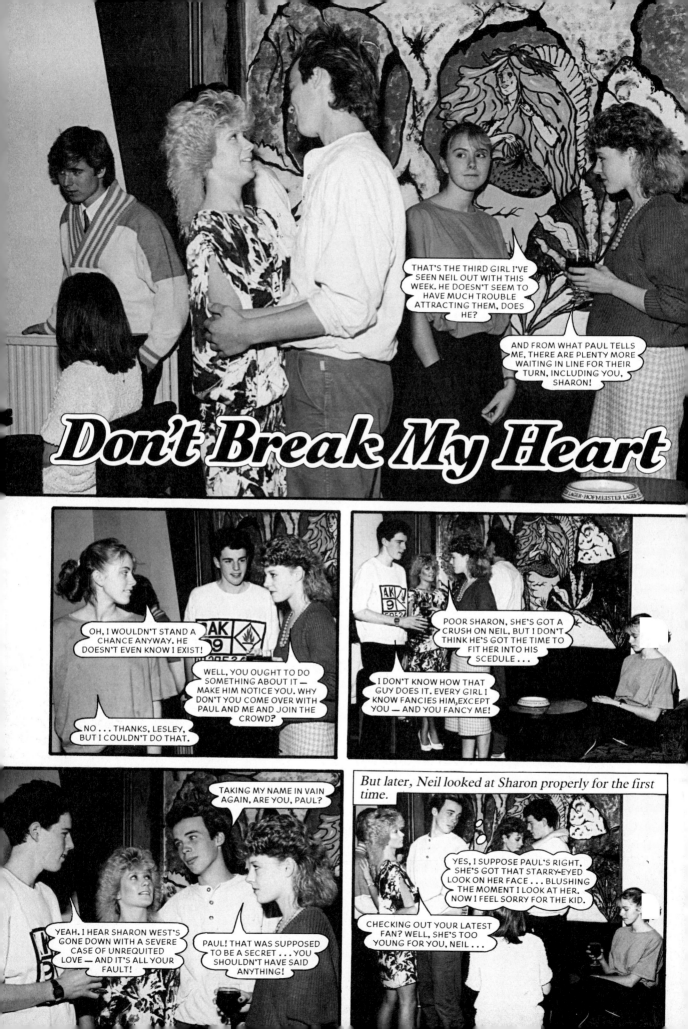

Don't Break My Heart

THAT'S THE THIRD GIRL I'VE SEEN NEIL OUT WITH THIS WEEK. HE DOESN'T SEEM TO HAVE MUCH TROUBLE ATTRACTING THEM, DOES HE?

AND FROM WHAT PAUL TELLS ME, THERE ARE PLENTY MORE WAITING IN LINE FOR THEIR TURN, INCLUDING YOU, SHARON!

OH, I WOULDN'T STAND A CHANCE ANYWAY. HE DOESN'T EVEN KNOW I EXIST!

WELL, YOU OUGHT TO DO SOMETHING ABOUT IT — MAKE HIM NOTICE YOU. WHY DON'T YOU COME OVER WITH PAUL AND ME AND JOIN THE CROWD?

NO . . . THANKS, LESLEY, BUT I COULDN'T DO THAT.

POOR SHARON, SHE'S GOT A CRUSH ON NEIL, BUT I DON'T THINK HE'S GOT THE TIME TO FIT HER INTO HIS SCEDULE . . .

I DON'T KNOW HOW THAT GUY DOES IT. EVERY GIRL I KNOW FANCIES HIM, EXCEPT YOU — AND YOU FANCY ME!

TAKING MY NAME IN VAIN AGAIN, ARE YOU, PAUL?

YEAH. I HEAR SHARON WEST'S GONE DOWN WITH A SEVERE CASE OF UNREQUITED LOVE — AND IT'S ALL YOUR FAULT!

PAUL! THAT WAS SUPPOSED TO BE A SECRET . . . YOU SHOULDN'T HAVE SAID ANYTHING!

But later, Neil looked at Sharon properly for the first time.

YES, I SUPPOSE PAUL'S RIGHT. SHE'S GOT THAT STARRY-EYED LOOK ON HER FACE . . . BLUSHING THE MOMENT I LOOK AT HER. NOW I FEEL SORRY FOR THE KID.

CHECKING OUT YOUR LATEST FAN? WELL, SHE'S TOO YOUNG FOR YOU, NEIL . . .

The next day Sharon found out that her secret was now common knowledge.

HI, SHARON. I HEAR YOU'VE JOINED THE REST OF US IN THE NEIL BATES FAN CLUB. NOT THINKING OF JUMPING THE QUEUE, I HOPE?

I ... BUT ... HOW DID YOU KNOW?

IT WAS ALL ROUND THE DISCO LAST NIGHT. SOMEONE EVEN TOLD NEIL YOU FANCY HIM.

I-I'LL NEVER BE ABLE TO FACE HIM AGAIN! WHAT AM I GOING TO DO?

NEVER MIND, IT MIGHT TURN OUT TO BE A GOOD THING. I MEAN, AT LEAST HE'S NOTICED YOU NOW.

WHICH IS MORE THAN HE'S DONE FOR ME, AND I'VE FANCIED HIM FOR MONTHS!

On the way home . . .

OH, NO! THERE HE IS! AND HE MUST BE AS EMBARRASSED AS I AM!

THERE'S THAT GIRL FROM THE DISCO — SHARON, I THINK HER NAME IS. I BET IT'D MAKE HER DAY IF I SPOKE TO HER . . .

And . . .

HI! SHARON, ISN'T IT? I SAW YOU AT THE DISCO LAST NIGHT . . .

OH, YES. I WAS THERE . . .

And, as he expected, she was over the moon . . .

I DIDN'T GET MUCH OF A CHANCE TO TALK TO YOU LAST NIGHT. BUT I WAS WONDERING, HOW ABOUT COMING OUT WITH ME SOME TIME?

OH, YEAH? WHAT'S THIS? SOME KIND OF JOKE?

I DON'T JOKE ABOUT THINGS LIKE THAT. I MEAN IT. I'D REALLY LIKE TO TAKE YOU OUT. YOU DO WANT TO COME, DON'T YOU?

YES, OF COURSE I DO . . .

I'LL SEE YOU AT THE COFFEE BAR TOMORROW AT HALF PAST EIGHT, THEN?

YES, I'LL BE FINISHED MY HOMEWORK BY THEN.

She could hardly believe it was happening. But for Neil, it was just another date, with just another girl — at first . . .

What Neil had thought would be a fairly dull evening turned out to be really interesting . . .

WELL, I DON'T MIND THE WORK AND I WANT TO GO ON TO COLLEGE.

YOU KNOW, MOST OF THE GIRLS I KNOW CAN'T WAIT TO LEAVE SCHOOL AND GET A JOB. I'VE NEVER MET SOMEONE LIKE YOU WHO ACTUALLY ENJOYS SCHOOL!

Continued on page 12

1. Just some of the line up, including presenter David Jensen, Spandau Ballet, Nick Heyward, Kim Wilde, Jennifer Rush and Slade . . . phew!

5. Doesn't say a lot — but hasn't he got a lovely smile?

6. Martin and Steve of Spandau are here — but who's who?

7. "Well I'm Steve. . ."

RAZZIN' AROUND THE CHRISTMAS TREE!

It was one of the loveliest December mornings I could remember. There was a chill in the air, but the sun shone brightly from a cornflower blue sky. It didn't really feel like Christmas!

As the train rolled into Newcastle, I couldn't help feeling how peaceful everything looked . . .

but little did I know that in one small corner of Newcastle, there was enough noise to drown out a football crowd at Wembley!

I could feel the excitement as I entered Studio 5. Tyne Tees had lined up a rota of *big* stars and this was to be *THE* Christmas pop event.

2. David Jensen lines up a host of stars to chat to. "Well, Kim, what have you been up to?"

3. "Loads of things . . . but I really haven't got time to hang about. Here's Nick."

4. "OK . . . I'll talk. . ."

8. "And I'm not!"

Right, enough of the indepth interviews, let's see some people doing what they do best!

9. Feargal Sharkey swings into action!

10. Feargal's backing singers . . .

▶▶▶▶

continued on page 14

Over the next few weeks Neil met Sharon as often as he could.

SO THAT'S WHAT NEIL'S DOING WITH HIS TIME LATELY!

I RECKON HE'S FALLEN FOR LITTLE SHARON — AND AFTER ALL HE SAID!

Everyone had to admit they made a lovely couple . . .

WELL, YOU DID IT, SHARON, YOU FINALLY LANDED NEIL. AND HE SEEMS TO HAVE FALLEN FOR YOU.

SHE'S RIGHT . . . HE HAS FALLEN FOR ME. IT'S HARD TO BELIEVE . . .

And it was obvious he'd changed . . .

HEY, FANCY COMING TO A PARTY TOMORROW NIGHT, NEIL? IT LOOKS LIKE BEING REALLY GOOD!

COME ON YOUR OWN, AND WE'LL INTRODUCE YOU TO SOME FANTASTIC GIRLS WE KNOW.

WELL, I'D LIKE TO COME, BUT ONLY IF I CAN BRING MY GIRLFRIEND WITH ME.

WELL, WHAT SHALL WE DO TOMORROW, SHARON? A PARTY, THE PICTURES, OR JUST A QUIET EVENING AT MY PLACE?

I . . . I DON'T KNOW, NEIL. I'VE GOT SOME WORK TO DO . . .

Later . . .

YOU'VE BEEN QUIET THIS EVENING, LOVE. THERE'S NOTHING WRONG, IS THERE?

I . . . WANTED TO TALK TO YOU, NEIL, ABOUT US. YOU SEE, I REALLY LIKE YOU — A LOT. AND THESE PAST WEEKS HAVE BEEN GREAT. BUT I KNOW YOU'RE GETTING SERIOUS ABOUT ME . . . AND I JUST CAN'T GET SERIOUS ABOUT ANYONE YET.

HEY, WHAT'S THIS? YOU CAN'T MEAN YOU WANT TO SPLIT UP? I THOUGHT YOU CARED FOR ME, SHARON?

I DO, NEIL. BUT EVERYTHING'S HAPPENED TOO FAST. I'VE GOT EXAMS AT SCHOOL . . . A LOT OF WORK TO DO . . . I REALLY THINK IT WOULD BE BEST IF I DIDN'T SEE YOU FOR A WHILE.

BUT I LOVE YOU, SHARON . . . WE'VE GOT SOMETHING SPECIAL . . .

I KNOW HOW MUCH YOU CARE, NEIL. I'M SORRY . . . BUT I JUST CAN'T GET INVOLVED . . . IT'S TOO SOON, NEIL . . . I NEED MORE TIME.

WELL, AT LEAST SHE DIDN'T SAY GOODBYE FOR EVER . . . PERHAPS IT WAS TOO SOON FOR HER. BUT I KNOW WE'VE GOT SOMETHING SPECIAL . . . I CAN ONLY HOPE THAT ONE DAY, SHARON WILL REALISE THAT TOO . . .

THE END

11. Jennifer Rush — "I'm so happy to be over here in little old England . . . "

12. ". . . And in such glamorous surroundings, too!"

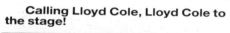

Calling Lloyd Cole, Lloyd Cole to the stage!

15. "OK . . . I'll just get this microphone stand fixed and we'll get started!"

16. "If I can remember the words!"

17. "Right . . . concentrate, if I remember the tune, I'll remember the words too!"

Now to two of the best performances of the day . . . Ladies and Gentlemen, the one and only — MADNESS.

13. Come on now, guys . . . pay attention!

14. All together now!

18. Lloyd gets it right — and drives the audience wild!

The day came to a close, and as everyone made their way out of the studio into the chilly night air, I could still hear the music and laughter . . . And guess what? It really did feel like Christmas now!

x

15

NAME:- Magne Furuholmen
DATE OF BIRTH:- 1/11/62
WORST JOB:- I worked in an arts centre for a while, and that was really boring. I also worked in a mental hospital ward — the same one as Morten . . .
LIKES:- My girlfriend.
HATES:- The fact that it's very difficult for foreign bands to be taken seriously by British audiences. I think that people like Baltimora and Opus give foreign bands a bad name.
1st LOVE: My first girlfriend was in the marching band that I was in at school. I liked her because she used to wear very short skirts!
1st PERFORMANCE:- With a band called Bridges, or maybe it was Spider Empire, back in Norway.
WHAT MAKES YOU ANGRY:- People who are intolerant.
IF THERE WAS A FIRE IN YOUR HOUSE, WHAT WOULD YOU MAKE A GRAB FOR FIRST: My Z.Z. Top keyring!
MOST EMBARRASSING MOMENT: Trying to impress a girl by swinging on a clothes line when I was a kid. I fell and broke my arm!

Starfile

NAME:- Pal Waaktaar
DATE OF BIRTH:- 6/9/61
WORST JOB:- Working in a factory, scrubbing floors.

LIKES: Good films like 'Psycho' and 'Amadeus'.
HATES: The winter. I hate being cold.
1st LOVE: I fell in love with one of my teachers. We had very pretty teachers at my school.
1st PERFORMANCE: With the first band that Mags and I formed. I can't remember what we were called.
WHAT MAKES YOU ANGRY: People who try to put me in a bad mood.
IF THERE WAS A FIRE IN YOUR HOUSE, WHAT WOULD YOU MAKE A GRAB FOR FIRST:- My family. They're very dear to me.
MOST EMBARRASSING MOMENT:- Forgetting how I went about writing songs when I was asked about it on live T.V. in America.

Starfile

NAME:- Morten Harket
DATE OF BIRTH:- 14/9/59
WORST JOB:- Well, I worked in a mental hospital for a year — that was a pretty crazy job. It's a wonder they didn't keep me inside.
LIKES:- Good films. I enjoyed watching 'Gorky Park' and 'The Moon In The Gutter' which Natassia Kinski starred in. She's one of my favourite actresses, actually. I also loved 'Electric Dreams' — even before I discovered that the director, Steve Barron, wanted to direct our videos.

HATES:- Being picked on. I was picked on by certain teachers when I was at school. They made my life a misery!
1st LOVE:- I had a bit of a crush on my teacher in first and second year at school. I was only six at the time!
1st PERFORMANCE:- I honestly can't remember! I was in a few lousy bands back in Norway — Soldier Blue, Mercy and Laelia Anceps, which is a kind of orchid.
WHAT MAKES YOU ANGRY:- When we arrive at a hotel and someone's forgotten to book it. It's very embarrassing, too.
IF THERE WAS A FIRE IN YOUR HOUSE, WHAT WOULD YOU MAKE A GRAB FOR FIRST:- Probably my camera — it's my most treasured possession. But, I really don't know — I've never been involved in a serious fire.
WHAT DO YOU MISS MOST ABOUT NORWAY:- Probably the scenery. I used to go sea fishing and walking through the woods when I lived at home. It's so exciting spotting real live reindeer.
BIGGEST SECRET:- Oh! I guess it must be the fact that we were relieved when we discovered that the 'Take On Me' video was going to be animated. The three of us were covered in spots when we filmed it!
MOST EMBARRASSING MOMENT:- I don't get embarrassed very easily — apart from when I've got to answer very personal questions!

a-ha

colourfield

bet you never thought dying could liven anything up, did you? Well, get hold of some boiler suits and overalls and see if a touch of dye can't give them a new lease of life! But in case you don't feel like splashing dye about, we've included a couple of suits from Fiori.

Details overleaf

1

2

field

3

Lovella (main shot)

Dyed orange boiler suit
Dyed blue shirt
10p from jumble sale.
Dyed purple vest T-shirt
10p from jumble sale.
Yellow Ski Pants
Paul Shriek as above.
Blue hat
From most sports shops.

1. Heidi (blonde)

Dyed blue overalls
Available from your local army
surplus or camping store.
Dyed blue shirt
From a selection at Flip, or wardrobes
of dads and brothers.
Yellow dyed T-shirt
From any shop selling T-shirts!
Red Ski Pants
Paul Shriek, Dean Street, Newcastle.
Write for details.
Red Hat
From most sports shops.

2. Heidi

Dyed yellow boiler suit
As blue overalls.
Dyed black and yellow T-shirt.
As No. 1.
Shoes and jewellery, model's own.

Lovella

White painter's bib and braces
As No. 1.
Black and white shirt
Paul Shriek as above.
Dyed Lab coat
As for overalls.
Yellow Ski Pants
As before.

3. Heidi

Bib and braces
From selection at Fiori. (Branches in
Newcastle, Carlisle and Dumfries).
T-shirt
As above.

Lovella

Flying suit
From Fiori
Belt
From a range at Paul Shriek.

21

We're not all natural beauties, so when it comes to party time, false bits can make all the difference! Hair, eyelashes, nails — nothing is real!

1 This is our model, Fiona, as she arrived at the studio, but you won't recognise her soon!

bits and pi

2 Now fully made-up, Fiona's hair has been brushed back and secured with a hairnet twisted tightly at the back. A strip of gauze is wound round the hairline to make extra sure no stray hairs escape!
The false eyelashes in this picture only cost a few pounds and you'll find a large selection in most good chemists. They come in a kit complete with glue and full instructions, but the best way to apply them is with tweezers. It also might be a good idea to ask a friend to help you, as it's quite a tricky job if you haven't tried them before!

ces

3 Wigs are a great way to give yourself a complete new look. You'd never guess this was Fiona, would you?
Wigs can cost anything upwards of £40, but we hired ours for only a few pounds for the day from a specialist wig shop.
And the great thing about wigs is that you can play around with them in the same way as you would normal hair.
We back-combed ours to give it fullness and tied tiny ribbons in it to brighten it up a bit!

4 Same girl, same make-up, different wig and completely different look!
We scrunched gel in to this wig to give it a wet look. There's more than a hint of the Joan Collins about this, isn't there?

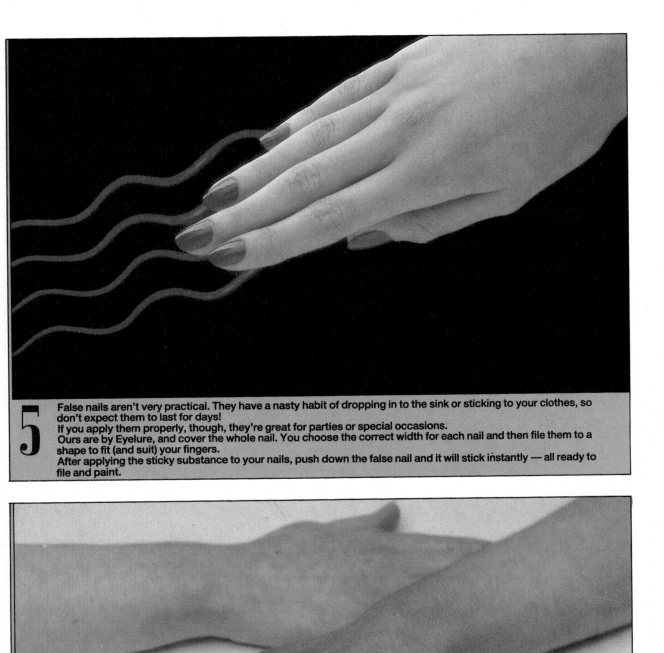

5 False nails aren't very practical. They have a nasty habit of dropping in to the sink or sticking to your clothes, so don't expect them to last for days!
If you apply them properly, though, they're great for parties or special occasions.
Ours are by Eyelure, and cover the whole nail. You choose the correct width for each nail and then file them to a shape to fit (and suit) your fingers.
After applying the sticky substance to your nails, push down the false nail and it will stick instantly — all ready to file and paint.

6 If you're looking a bit pale, fake tan could be just the thing for you.
Fake tans contain chemicals which stick to the skin cells and turn them a golden colour, usually within four or five hours.
So, if you're feeling a bit pale and boring, grab a bottle and go for gold!

Make-up and wigs dressed by Suzy Bailey.   Wigs hired from A and A Hair Studios, 9/10 Tanfield, Inverleith Row, Edinburgh.

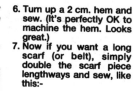

MATERIAL GIRL

Introducing PATCHES exclusive skirt and top! You won't win any prizes from your needlework mistress for the sewing, but who cares? Your skirt will look terrific, take half an hour to make and cost around £4 — even less if you're clever and scour the local market for remnants!

So what are you waiting for?

Let's begin with the skirt . . .

INSTRUCTIONS FOR SKIRT & SCARF

You will need:
1 metre jersey fabric, approx. 150 cm. wide
1 metre elastic, approx. 2 cm. wide
Matching thread.
Now then:
1. Measure your hips and add on. 6 cm.
Measure (on yourself) the length you want the finished skirt to be and add on 5 cm.
2. Your length of jersey will probably be doubled. Open it out and cut your skirt and scarf pieces out like this:-

3. Fold your skirt piece in half lengthways, measure

in 2.5 cm. from the raw edges and seam, like this:-

(The seam will run down the back of your skirt.)

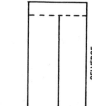

4. Turn over and sew the top 3 cm. for the waistband, leaving a 5 cm. gap unsewn over the back seam, like this:-

5. Take your waist measurement MINUS 3 cm. and cut a length of elastic to this measurement.
Pin a safety pin to one end of the elastic and thread it right through the waistband and out the other side. Overlap the ends of the elastic by 3 cm. and sew together firmly.
Then sew up the 5 cm. gap.

6. Turn up a 2 cm. hem and sew. (It's perfectly OK to machine the hem. Looks great.)
7. Now if you want a long scarf (or belt), simply double the scarf piece lengthways and sew, like this:-

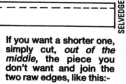

If you want a shorter one, simply cut, *out of the middle*, the piece you don't want and join the two raw edges, like this:-

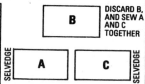

then proceed as for a long scarf.
Turn your scarf right side out and there you are. Don't try and hem the raw selvedges — you'll find they look just like fringing.
8. Press your skirt and scarf on the WRONG side under a damp cloth, otherwise you'll get seam marks showing which will spoil all your hard work.
9. Now dress yourself up, go out, and show off. No-one'll believe you made it yourself!

This has to be the most versatile top around! You can make it in any material you like — soft silky jersey, crisp cotton, wool for warmth — you name it, your top will look good in it.

And it's dead easy to make because you can use your machine for every stitch on it (or you could do the whole thing by hand and end up with an haute couture top)!

But the best thing of all is that it only takes one metre of fabric!

You will need:-
1 piece of brown paper or newspaper
1 metre fabric, 112 cm. wide (Fabric wider than 112 cm. will be fine, but don't use one that is *less* than 112 cm.)
1 metre matching (or neutral) bias binding
Matching thread.

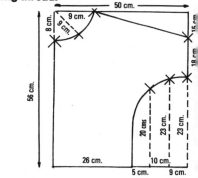

INSTRUCTIONS FOR TOP

1. You could measure and mark the pattern straight on to your material, but we think it's worth making a paper pattern first. It only takes a few minutes, and once you've made it you can use it again and again.
So — you'll need a piece of brown paper, or newspaper. Cut the paper to measure 50 centimetres wide and 56 centimetres long, then measure and mark it up like this:-

continued on page **57**

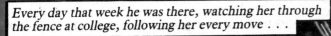

Every day that week he was there, watching her through the fence at college, following her every move . . .

After The Love Has Gone...

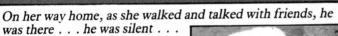

On her way home, as she walked and talked with friends, he was there . . . he was silent . . .

But whenever she turned to look . . . he was gone!

THAT'S ODD! I COULD'VE SWORN THERE WAS SOMEONE WATCHING ME . . . BUT I WAS WRONG. THERE'S NO-ONE THERE.

THAT'S THREE TIMES THIS WEEK I'VE HAD THE FUNNIEST FEELING THAT SOMEONE'S FOLLOWING ME . . .

THAT'S WHAT YOU GET FOR GOING TO DRAMA SCHOOL. THEY SAY YOU NEED A WILD IMAGINATION TO BE A GOOD ACTRESS!

Jill was already a good actress . . .

THAT WAS A GREAT READING, JILL. YOU REALLY GOT INTO THE CHARACTER. YOU'RE GOING TO BE TERRIFIC IN THE PART.

29

30

THE END

31

"NO, no, no," I said decisively, "a thousand times no."

"Oh come on, Claire," my Aunt Dotty urged. "Don't be like that. You know we can't disappoint the old folk; and you help with the panto every year anyway."

"Helping behind the scenes is one thing. Playing Cinderella is another."

Aunt Dot grinned.

Three weeks before the annual panto for the Old Folk's Home, Karen Blake, who was to be Cinderella, had caught chickenpox from her little brother, and left Aunt Dotty without her leading lady. Never one to be stuck for long, my aunt was on the hunt for some mug to step in — and she'd chosen me.

"Well, much as I hate to disappoint you, Aunt Dot, you'll have to find someone else."

"And that's your last word?"

"Yes."

"I'll see you tomorrow, half past seven, at the theatre."

☆ ☆

As it turned out, she came to collect me in the car in case I really didn't turn up.

"There's a very nice young man playing Buttons," she said tentatively.

"Who's Buttons?" I said sulkily,

but my spirits rose slightly.

"He's Cinderella's father's servant, and he's in love with you," Aunt Dot informed me, sensing my interest. "Really, you'll like him, Claire. His name's Peter; he's got a lovely voice."

Fantastic, I thought bitterly. As long as he's got a nice voice, what do I care if he looks like a Pogue?

Aunt Dot parked the car and hustled me in the stage door. A crowd of teenagers were sitting around on the stage, obviously waiting for Aunt Dot to arrive.

"Right, boys and girls, this is Claire, and she's going to be Cinderella, so . . ."

That was as much as I heard. I'd

seen him! He was sitting at the far end of the stage cross-legged, reading a script. He had longish, fine blond hair, he was wearing a faded stripy shirt and he was lovely! Ooh, thank you, Aunt Dot, thank you . . .

"Claire? Are you listening to me? This is Peter, who's playing Buttons."

Confused, I looked from Aunt Dot to a gruesome Pogue-like being at her side. She had to be kidding . . .

Peter was very friendly, and immediately offered to help with my lines. After fifteen minutes of his scintillating conversation — Peter, Peter and more Peter — I was ready to shove my libretto down his throat

erella

shut him up. Only the thought of the gorgeous specimen I had seen earlier kept me in the building.

Finally, though, during the teabreak, he came over to talk to me.

"It's Claire, isn't it?" he said, with a smile that made me sit down before I fell down. "It's really good of you to step in at the last minute like this. The show would have fallen through without your help."

"I'm terrified," I told him miserably, looking for sympathy. Instead he grinned, in much the same way as Aunt Dot had done.

"You'll do just fine, Claire. Dotty's a good judge of talent underneath that scatter-brained exterior. By the way, I'm Gertrude — your Ugly Sister."

but Carol-Anne was delighted. She was the prompter, and she hadn't had much work to do for weeks.

Another problem was Peter. He'd really taken a fancy to me, and he never left me on my own for more than five minutes during the evening. I dropped about a million hints, but I didn't have the heart to tell him outright that he looked like a Pogue and would he please get lost, and consequently he continued to hang around, telling me about himself non-stop, much to the amusement of Gertrude and Aunt Dot. On stage, he was alarmingly convincing when declaring his love for Cinderella. I tried appealing to Aunt Dot, but she just laughed.

"But what about me?" I almost wailed.

got so dizzy I stood on the hem of my dress, and Gertrude and I landed in an ungainly heap on the floor. We both found it pretty funny and none too unpleasant — until I tried to get up. My ankle was swelling up furiously.

Peter, of course, had done first aid, so he tied up my injured foot with a bandage soaked in cold water, and I cursed and muttered and sulked, and Gertrude tried not to laugh.

Aunt Dotty, however, was not discouraged.

"A bad dress rehearsal means a good first night," she declared, helping me out of my balldress.

"Well, tomorrow night is going to be spectacular, then," laughed Gertrude. "Come on, Claire, I'll take you home."

☆   ☆

Gertrude was right, as it turned out. The show went brilliantly, and the old folk loved it. Afterwards, we had a party at Aunt Dot's, and I felt friendly towards everyone, even Peter and especially Gertrude.

I was sitting on my own, watching everyone else dancing, when a voice beside me made me jump.

"Shall we see if it fits?"

I turned to see Gertrude kneeling beside me, holding the shoe I had taken off the night before when I'd hurt my ankle.

"Of course it won't fit, you idiot," I laughed. "My ankle's all swollen and bandaged."

"Oh well," he grinned, "it doesn't matter anyway. I recognise you. You were the one at the ball last night who . . ."

"Captured your heart and whom you will love for evermore?" I hazarded hopefully.

". . . who knocked me flying and made me bruise my backside. However," he continued, as I started to laugh, "I'm willing to forgive you if you come out with me tomorrow."

"What about Peter?" I couldn't help asking.

Gertrude indicated Peter and Jenny Davidson, who was playing the Prince.

"Looks like he's found his Prince Charming at last."

I've been seeing Gerry for almost five months. But I still call him Gertrude sometimes, even now.

At the time I doubted that anyone could make *him* look ugly, but you'd be surprised what a red wig and green freckles can do for a bloke.

That night, after the rehearsal, I went home and locked myself in my bedroom to learn all my lines. I was determined to impress Gertude, and really make a go of this pantomime.

"That's it!" I yelled at my sister, at two o'clock that morning. "I'm *sure* I know them all now!"

I could hardly wait for the next rehearsal. Gertrude and Aunt Dot were going to be delighted.

We rehearsed every night the next week. Gertrude was highly amused, Aunt Dot was in despair,

"Just bear with us till the panto's over. We'll sort it all out then."

To be honest, it wasn't so much Peter that was worrying me as the thought that Gertrude might think I actually liked the little creep. Every time I spoke to Peter I could be ruining my chances even further with him!

It was at the final dress rehearsal, the night before the show, that I found myself in Gertrude's arms at last. We were doing the Ball scene, and although I was doing my level best to waltz gracefully round the stage with the Prince, I had to be careful to hold up my dress, which was still a bit too long. However, as she whirled me round and round, I

first time for everything

●Whether it's your first kiss, your first date or your first job, you're bound to be nervous — then after it's over, you'll wonder what all the fuss was about! Well, Patches comes to your aid yet again and gives you a few hints to follow the first time!

first party

A million things will go through your mind when you get the invitation to your first real party. What do you wear? Who else is going? Will everyone be older than you? What if the guy you fancy ends up with someone else and even worse — what if you end up with someone you don't fancy?

It's natural to get into a state before your first party, but it's important not to get so uptight that it becomes more of a chore than a pleasure, and you're dreading it rather than looking forward to it.

Wear what you feel good in, but make sure you're not going to look too different from the other people there. For instance, if most of the girls in your class still think that John Travolta is *really* cool, then don't turn up looking like Siouxsie. You don't have to wear a get-up from Grease, though —just compromise a bit.

Ask whoever invited you who else is going. There's bound to be someone you know, so arrange to go with them. If you can't, remember that lots of other people will be going on their own too — there's nothing wrong in it, and you're bound to meet up with some of your friends there.

When you walk in for the first time, you'll probably find it a bit daunting. The room will be dark, the music will be deafening, and the place will be full of people that you've never seen in your life before — or so you think. They'll be completely wrapped up in their own affairs, and won't appear to have noticed your existence.

Don't turn round and walk out! Have a look round. There are sure to be one or two people standing about looking as shy or lost as you! Go over and talk to them. Ask where to get a drink. Pretty soon you'll be enjoying the whole thing; and in a year or so, when you've been to lots of parties, you'll forget that you were ever nervous about this one!

first date

Oh blimey, here we go again! What will you wear? Where will you go? What will you talk about? You might even think that the first date is even worse than the first party, because you can't leave or hide in the crowd, since there's only you and him!

But don't worry. He'll probably be as nervous as you! If you haven't already planned where to go, suggest the cinema if you think you aren't going to be able to make conversation. But you'll be surprised at how much you'll find to talk about. Ask about his family, his taste in music, his schoolwork or his job. Once you've broken the ice there won't be any problem! And if he doesn't ask you for another date, don't worry — there are plenty more where he came from!

first boyfriend

Going out with your first steady boyfriend is a great experience. You want to be together all the time, and when you can't be with him, you talk about him, dream about him and smile at everyone who comes near you.

When you're with him, discos have never seemed such exciting places! You want to show him off to all your friends, take him to meet the family, get to know all his mates.

But it's important not to spend *too* much time with him. Too much of a good thing soon bores you — and if it doesn't bore you, it'll bore him. Make sure you don't abandon your friends either — set a little time aside for them too. Let's face it, if your best mate spent all her time with her new boyfriend and forgot you existed, you'd be pretty upset, too!

Try not to build your whole life around this guy, because if and when you finally split up, you'll be badly hurt — especially since you've no previous experience of coping with a break-up.

And if you do split up sooner than you expected, just remember that he's not the only nice guy in the world — there are lots of them, and you'll probably find another much more quickly than you imagine!

first interview

What do I wear? What do I say? What will they ask? Sound familiar? Don't panic! Everyone gets in a bit of a state before their first interview — but if you remember a few simple points, everything should be OK!

Firstly, interviewers are human. They have had to go through interviews too, and they know how you're feeling. Don't be frightened of them — they're not trying to scare you off!

Try to find out a little about the company before you go for the interview. It shows that you're keen and interested, and that's a mark in your favour.

You don't have to dress like your gran, but don't go to the other extreme until you know what the company's policy is on dress. You can look modern and attractive without scaring the socks off the interviewer!

Finally, try to keep the conversation going. Don't just answer yes and no. Ask questions about the firm yourself. And if you don't get the job, it's not because there's anything wrong with you — it's just because that particular job didn't suit you!

Wendy walking Norrie through the bus station to see how he reacts.

Walkin' The Dog

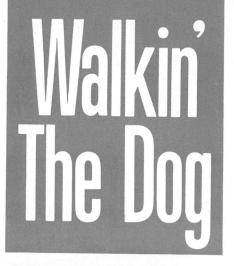

Crossing the road . . . but Norrie seems more interested in posing for the camera

One of the greatest charities in Britain must be the Guide Dogs for the Blind. It's a cause that everyone wants to help with, but it's also something that a lot of people don't know too much about. We visited Wendy Ramsey at the Forfar Guide Dogs Centre to find out a bit more . . .

TRAINING guide dogs must be one of the most rewarding jobs around, and one that many people would love to become involved with; but not many know where to start.

"You apply for a job through your local Guide Dog centre," Wendy explained. "Exam passes aren't really necessary — you gain the qualifications you need through the centre itself. To start working with the dogs, you have to be 17, and you start working in kennels. To actually train the dogs you have to be 20."

This perhaps doesn't sound very encouraging for a sixteen-year-old school leaver, but there is another way to become involved with guide dogs in the meantime.

"Puppywalking is voluntary," Wendy told us. "It means that someone takes a pup into their home for a year, and brings it up just like a normal pet — housetraining it and getting it used to traffic and so on. Then we take it back and start the real training."

To become a puppywalker, you apply to the nearest Guide Dog centre, and someone will come to interview your family

Coming down steep steps takes all Norrie's concentration!

Russell and Mitzi the kitten.

"What's that cat doing *now?*"

to see whether you're suitable.

"There are lots of things to be considered," Wendy told us. "For instance, the pups come from special breeding centres, and are already named when we get them, so we try not to put a pup in a household where there is someone of the same name. Also, if a family live in the middle of nowhere, then a puppy isn't going to have much chance to get used to city life. However, if the family are willing to take the dog into town even once a week, that's fine."

☆ ☆ ☆

Mrs Middleton has looked after nine pups for the centre, and because she is very experienced, she sometimes takes on difficult puppies who might be as old as five months.

"I've had Norrie for two months," she told us. "He's six months old. He was a little bit naughty when he came to me

Trips to the pet shop make sure Norrie is used to other animals.

Yvonne Anderson is 13, and Russell is the third pup her family have had. As well as young people like Yvonne and her sister being in the home, the Andersons have a kitten and a budgie for Russell to get used to.

"He still bullies the kitten a bit," Yvonne admitted, "but mostly he's very good. I take him up to the town, and on buses, things like that. He still hasn't seen a horse or a cow yet, though!"

Yvonne realises how much greater the responsibility is, looking after a guide dog as opposed to an ordinary pet.

"You find you're more conscientious. I'm always scared of losing Russell in the park."

But doesn't Yvonne find it sad when it's time for the dogs to go back to the centre?

"Oh yes, of course. But if the dog is rejected, or when he's too old to work, you as the puppywalker get first refusal on him."

We asked Yvonne if she would like to take a job at the Guide Dog Centre when she's old enough.

"I've thought about it," she agreed. "It's either that or becoming a vet."

Training guide dogs is a very demanding occupation, but very worthwhile. And puppywalking is a very important stage in the dog's career, because it's during this time that they must learn how to walk on the lead and how to behave in the house.

"We've never managed to have the whole family together to see a pup going away," Yvonne's mum said. "We just can't face it! It's terribly sad when a dog has to go back — but it's very rewarding to think that you've started off the training of a guide dog."

— chewing things, and stealing food, but he's a reformed character now!"

So how did Mrs Middleton manage to reform Norrie?

"You must prevent boredom. I never shut dogs up unless I can trust them, and I like to keep them round me all the time.

"When you're given your first puppy, the centre issues you with a feeding guide, and some basic do's and don'ts. Every so often, someone from the centre, in Mrs Middleton's case, Wendy, comes round to check on the puppy's progress, and takes him out for a walk.

"When the puppy finally has to go back to the centre, a replacement is found for you as soon as possible, providing you want one!

"We have an 'award' scheme for the old hands," Wendy laughed. "Once you've had five pups, you get a bronze award, after ten a silver and after fifteen, a gold."

☆ ☆ ☆

"Lead us not into temptation . . ."

That is one strong-willed dog!

All work and no play . . .

Feeding time at the Centre for Jo, Jessie and Sacha.

39

ear

These pop stars are *always* bitching about each other — and no wonder, with some of the rubbish that gets in the charts.

We gathered together a group of would-be, used-to-be and will-be pop stars and asked them which records make *them* cringe . . .

DIVINE:

'I am (I'm Me)' by Twisted Sister.

"This group looks terrible and they sound even worse. I hate head-banging music and Twisted Sister are noisier and more tuneless than any other Heavy Metal group I know of. They make a big act of being outrageous but really they're as tame as mice."

MARTIN FRY of ABC:

'The Wild Boys' by Duran Duran.

"Was this supposed to be a tough record or something? Sorry, boys, but it sounded really feeble to me."

42

ACHE!

PAUL KING:

'Shaddup Your Face' by Joe Dolce.

"Because it kept Ultravox off Number One with 'Vienna'."

SUGGS of MADNESS:

Anything by Meatloaf.

"It's music for bank clerks. I remember seeing him live once. I'll never forget the audience. It was just like walking into a bank."

ADAM ANT:

The Latin American version of **'Dog Eat Dog'**.

"I've never liked those Top 20 compilation albums which have session men singing all the hits, but when somebody in Latin America did this Adam and the Ants hit I could hardly believe my ears. They tried to sing it in English but clearly they didn't understand the language and they kept getting all the words wrong!"

KIM WILDE:

'Wherever I Go Whatever I do' by Hazell Dean.

"I don't like the melody or the lyric and I'm not too keen on the way she sings it either!"

STEPHEN DUFFY:

'Rat Rapping' by Roland Rat.

"That was probably the most awful record ever made in the entire history of popular music. Back to the sewers, Roland!"

NICK HEYWARD:

'Agadoo' by Black Lace.

"What a rotten record. It must be at the top of nearly everyone's list of most hated music. The worst thing about it is that it's so *catchy*. Oh no, I think I'm going to start singing it! *Ag-a-do-do-do* . . . eeeek! Throw water over me, someone!"

MARK KING of LEVEL 42:

"Oh dear, I'm not sure really. We don't make a big thing about records we don't like, we just ignore them. Has anyone mentioned **'Superman'** by Black Lace yet? No-one — you're kidding! OK then, put me down for that, and remember, I was the first one to say it. I'd have thought *everyone* said that. Not that Black Lace mind, they did very well out of it, thank you."

PRINCESS:

"'**Grandad'** by Clive Dunn. What do you mean I'm the first person to choose that? *Everyone* hates it. Maybe they just couldn't think of it at the time. I'll be humming it for days now, because it's one of those records that sticks in your mind for ages. If I start humming it under my breath on 'Top Of The Pops' that will be *your* fault!"

SIMON LE BON:

"Without a doubt it's **'Geno'** by Dexys Midnight Runners. I hated it the day I heard it, and I've grown to seriously hate it ever since. I won't allow it to be played at home at *all*! If you want to know what Kevin Rowland's voice should sound like, listen to a song called 'Everything Is Tuesday' by an old soul group called Chairman Of The Board. A bit of real soul for you, not this imitation junk."

FEARGAL SHARKEY:

"Anything by The Pogues! I can't remember any of the songs, just that the sound is more than enough. Death to fake Irish folk music. Let's have the real thing or nothing at all, please!"

ROLAND GIFT of FINE YOUNG CANNIBALS:

"My hated record is quite old, maybe you won't know it, it's called **'Lola'** by the Kinks. It has a line in it about drinking champagne and it tasting like cherry cola. I mean, what sort of a lyric is that? The tune is pretty naff as well. I like something with a bit of wallop about it. This just runs on and away, rather like dirty bath water. Is that too cruel? You agree! That's OK, then."

PETER POWELL:

'**Orville's Song'** by Keith Harris and Orville.

"That silly duck practically drives me up the wall."

LLOYD COLE:

"From a long list of hated records, I have to say **'Superman'** by Black Lace. Someone's had that? OK then, I'll have **'Rabbit'** by Chas And Dave, a more pointless record has yet to be recorded. I have nightmares about being shipwrecked with just a record player, and only one record, and that's it. I usually wake up screaming."

STEVE BRONSKI of BRONSKI BEAT:

"The Communards' first single **'You Are My World'** was dreadful! We all wondered what it would be like, and we were very shocked when we heard it. It's so over-the-top isn't it? I much preferred Jimi's voice over an electronic sound like ours, but still that's his choice, but we all thought it was a bit of a joke in the end. A bad one."

DEE C. LEE:

"That Sting single **'Russians'**, I've never liked that at all. I think it's all so simple. Of course Russians love their children — most people do, but that doesn't mean they won't carry on with their ideas about controlling the rest of the world, given half a chance. I think Sting is old enough to know better, and I know he can write far better songs than this load of old junk. OK?"

CAPTAIN SENSIBLE:

Anything by Jonathan King.
"What can I say? . . .
Bleughhhh!!!!"

PAUL McCARTNEY:

"I honestly have to say that I don't really *hate* anyone's records. When you've had as much muck thrown at you for records you've slaved over for months as I have, you learn to be tolerant. I'll tell you a record I mildly dislike if that's OK. — **'Santa Claus Is Coming To Town'** by Bruce Springsteen. I don't like it because I like to get *my* Christmas records in the charts, and I don't like to have competition. Only joking, Bruce, the rest of your records are really *gear* as we Liverpudlians say."

face FACTS

PROTRUDING EYES

Impulsive and demanding, you do everything without thinking, which often lands you in *big* trouble! You're a great person to go out with, because you always enjoy yourself. Even when you're down, you can put on a happy face, so you're a really popular person and have loads of friends.

UPTURNED EYES

You have a wicked sense of fun, and love to amuse everyone around you — sometimes by being bitchy about others! You don't really mean it, though — you get on well with most people. You may dress rather differently as you're a bit of an extrovert.

LARGE EYES

You are intelligent and creative, but can be really short-tempered at times. Warm and generous, you are sometimes too kind and let others take advantage of your good nature. Attractive to the opposite sex, you're a bit of a flirt, too.

DEEP-SET EYES

You're probably very intellectual, but you don't like to show off your cleverness. Fairly quiet, people often don't realise how nice you are. Make more of an effort to make new friends. Very honest and trustworthy, you expect others to be the same and are often disappointed.

SMALL EYES

You're kind and gentle, and prefer to have a few close friends you can really trust, rather than a huge circle of acquaintances. You lack confidence in yourself, which you really shouldn't, because you're one of the nicest people around.

You might think you're giving nothing away — but it's all there in your face! Your eyes and your mouth reveal the secrets of your character!

DOWNTURNED EYES

You're one of the most loyal, trustworthy people around and people often come to you with their probelms because you're so sympathetic. You dream a lot and because you spend so much time thinking about things, you very rarely get around to actually doing anything! Once you do, though, you're very organised and thorough.

EVEN MOUTH

An even mouth, when both lips are of equal size, shows that you are articulate and friendly. You tend to talk too much and too often and you're not someone who can be trusted with a secret. Even so, you're always surrounded by friends — and boys!

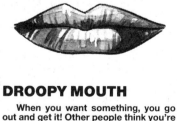

DROOPY MOUTH

When you want something, you go out and get it! Other people think you're lucky, but you're not really — you just work hard and reap the rewards.

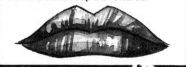

SMALL MOUTH

Fairly quiet, you probably don't have loads of friends, but the ones you do have never fall out with you. You value your privacy and don't mind being on your own at all. You're a very caring person and generous with both money and emotions.

UPTURNED MOUTH

If your mouth turns up at the corners, you are artistic and creative. You tend to look a bit smug and you can be a bit big-headed at times. Still, you're attractive, so mabye you've a right to be!

WIDE MOUTH

You're very strong-minded and can be a bit intimidating. Once you decide to do something, no-one can change your mind. You're probably very fond of sports and animals.

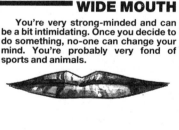

HEART SHAPED MOUTH

Nothing makes you really angry. You can always see both sides of an argument, but this makes you a bit indecisive as you never know which side to take. You're quiet and gentle, and make a really good friend.

NO FOOL FOR LOVE – OR ARE YOU?

Are you the sort of girl who believes everything that's said to her? Do you trust your boyfriend blindly, or do you sometimes get a little bit suspicious? Boys are devious characters, y'know — you've got to be up to all their tricks! Try our quiz and see whether or not boys take you for a fool!

1. You're just putting on your final coat of mascara when the phone rings, and it's him. "Hello, love," he says. "Look, I'm really sorry, but I can't make it tonight. My poor old gran's not too well, so I've got to go round and see her. Just staying in then, are you?" Do you say:
a) "Yeah, I will. Unless you'd like me to come to your gran's. No? Well, tell her I hope she's better soon."
b) "That'll be right, mate. I'm going out with Karen and Jenny, and if I bump into you at the disco with Tarty Tracey, I'll break your jaw."
c) Nothing, but spend the night wondering if he was telling the truth?

2. You're over at your best friend's house, and she's in floods of tears. Her boyfriend had phoned her to say his gran wasn't well, so he couldn't see her, and she'd found out he was out with Tarty Tracey! Do you . . .
c) Laugh and say, "Yeah, John tries that one every so often too. Gives you a good excuse for a date with Sexy Simon, though."
b) Start to wonder, but know you could never get up the nerve to confront your own boyfriend about it.
a) Pat her shoulder and say proudly, "That's really awful. John would *never* do anything like that!"?

3. You've been waiting for him for an hour and a half in the belting rain. When he finally arrives, he does have an excuse . . . "Well, y'see, I was running down the road to meet you, and what should I see but a runaway horse galloping down the road towards me, and its rider was screaming for help. So what could I do but throw myself at it, grab the reins and stop it? The girl was

so grateful, she gave me a big kiss!" Well, sure enough, there's lipstick on his face. What do you do?
b) Decide he must be telling the truth. Well, he wouldn't tell you a ridiculous story like that unless it was true, would he? Would he . . . ?
a) Tell him how brave and wonderful he is, at the same time thinking how honest it was to mention the kiss she gave him . . .
c) Collapse in hysterics, and treat him to a night at the disco for giving you such a laugh.

4. There you are, down at the disco, giving it all that to "Tarzan Boy", when who should walk in but your beloved, with his arm around a skinny blonde. What do you do?
a) Rush over to them, and say, "Oh hi! You must be John's cousin Sandra that he's always telling me about!"
b) Run and hide in the loos. He'll tell you about his cousin tomorrow — if she is his cousin . . .
c) Punch him in the mouth.

5. The exams are getting closer, and he tells you he'd like to cool it for a couple of weeks so he can do some revising. "Funny," you think, "it's never worried him before." Do you:
b) Phone him every hour on the hour to check up on him,
a) Think how clever and studious he is, whilst remarking on the amazing similarity between him and the guy walking past your house with his arm round John's cousin Sandra,
c) Get on the phone straight away and ask Sexy Simon for a date?

6. What would you do if he told you he loved you?
a) Melt into his arms and tell you love

him, too; and of *course* you don't mind lending him a tenner so that he can take his cousin Sandra to the pictures . . .
b) Want to believe him, but find it difficult?
c) Say, "Do you really? Lend us a tenner, then, I'm taking my cousin Simon to the pictures tonight!"

7. What do you think when you look into his eyes?
b) "I wonder if he's been out with that Tracey behind my back!"
a) "What a beautiful shade of blue his eyes are. I'm so lucky to have a guy like him."
c) "They're going to be a lovely shade of purple when I've blacked them for him. Teach him to go out with Tarty Tracey behind my back!"?

CONCLUSIONS

MOSTLY As: You're like a little spaniel, you are; you believe everything he says, and don't ever question it! If your best mate's boyfriend told her stories like that, you wouldn't expect her to swallow them, would you? You'll just have to remember that everyone's not as nice as you!

MOSTLY Bs: You're not *exactly* a fool — you suspect he's telling you a lot of rot, but you haven't got the nerve to talk to him about it! Don't be afraid to confront him about it — he's got no right to take you for a fool!

MOSTLY Cs: Well, one thing's for sure — no-one's going to take you for a fool! More likely you're the one who's taking a loan of your boyfriend! Don't be too hard, though — there are some nice guys in the world, you know — and if you find one, you won't keep him for long by treating him like dirt!

KISSING is something that seems like the hardest thing in the world — until you've tried it, then you wonder what all the fuss was about.

Everybody enjoys doing it eventually — and most people also have at least *one* experience of a kiss that did nothing for them whatsoever, apart from leaving them thinking "yeuch!". But when you get it right, kissing can be a great way of expressing certain feelings without bothering to search for the right words.

Yet, natural as it is, kissing's something that a lot of people worry about — boys included. Our mail sack for the problem page always includes letters from people worrying about being kissed, not being kissed, *how* to kiss . . . so it can't always come *that* naturally!

The first thing to remember is that kissing shouldn't be a duty — it should be enjoyable. And if you don't feel like having a snogging session surrounded by two hundred people at a disco the first time you meet a new guy — then don't! Some boys are very keen to demonstrate their kissing technique even when they've only met you for five minutes — the only problem is, it's often more like an advanced course in mouth-to-mouth resuscitation.

The best way to fend off a crazed octopus is to laugh it off as pleasantly as you can, and say, "Hold it — not yet!" In other words, you don't *have* to be kissed, until you feel like it — it's up to you! Better just to say, laughingly, something like, "I'd prefer to get to know you just a little first!" rather than nervously dodging a pair of eager lips all evening!

But, when you do get round to kissing a new guy — and that doesn't usually take longer than the first date — should it *always* be wonderful, all fireworks, dreamy music and shivers down the spine?

Well, it would be nice if it were always that way — but it isn't, especially with a first kiss. Sometimes, for instance, you find you can't seem to concentrate, and you start thinking the daftest things, and end up almost

bursting out laughing in the middle of it! Or sometimes one or both of you might feel awkward and tense, or silly, or one of you might break off kissing just as the other one's starting to enjoy it — it happens all the time! It's just a matter of getting "tuned in" to each other. So if your first kiss with a new guy isn't a wonderful success, don't worry, things will improve with practice!

"I DON'T KNOW HOW TO KISS!"

Most people have felt this at one stage, even if they've never actually said it. But unfortunately, kissing's not really an activity you can learn by the book — like dancing, dating, getting on with boys in general, it's something that eventually falls into place, with a bit of experience.

There's no point in having long kissing sessions unless you're actually *enjoying* it — and the best way to do that is to relax. Just close your eyes, take a deep breath, and let it happen naturally.

Try not to think *too* hard about what you're doing, and make sure you're not holding yourself tense and rock-like. If you *act* as if you're quite cool and relaxed, you'll actually start to feel more relaxed. And if you like the guy in question, there's every chance you'll really enjoy kissing each other, without trying too hard. So now you know how to kiss . . .

kissing to be c

OW KISSABLE RE YOU?

Of course, if a guy fancies you at he'll be pretty keen to kiss you — there are certain things you can o make sure it's pleasant for him! Your teeth, for example, should he starting point of your beauty ine before going out on a date. should visit your dentist every six nths, treat yourself to a decent hbrush and replace it regularly — way your teeth'll soon be in their possible condition.

Unhealthy or poorly cleaned h can be a major cause of bad ath — as can smoking, eating y or garlicky food, and alcohol. ing, and not drinking enough s can also dry up your mouth and ve you less than delightful to kiss ry eating something like an apple a pear if you can't get to your hbrush before a date — it should !

You'll also be a lot more kissable ur lips are smooth and soft — products such as Blisteze, apstick, Cymes and Blisteze Blistick keep them that way, and they rk virtually at once. Ordinary tick can also help prevent dryness n the sun, wind, cold and central- ating, especially the moisturising es.

If you follow these tips, you'll e no problems — it'll be bliss en you kiss!

classical gas

9. "You got your mother in a whirl, she's not sure if you're a boy or a girl, hey babe, your hair's all right, hey babe let's go out tonight."

So you reckon you're a musical mastermind? Well, test your knowledge with our classic records quiz!

coming back now, cruel Heathcliff, my one dream, my only master."

10. "If I were a sculptor, or then again, no, or a man who makes potions in a travelling show, well I know it's not much, but it's the best I can do, my gift is my song, and this one's for you."

Section 1 Lyrics

1. "The squaw is with the corporal, she is tied against a tree, she doesn't mind the language,it's the beating she don't need, she lets loose all the horses while the corporal is asleep."

2. "Bless my cotton socks I'm in the news, the king sits on his face but it's all assumed, all wrapped the same, all wrapped up the same, they can't have it, you can't have it, I can't have it ooh."

3. "So what's the use of robbery when nothing is worth taking? It's kind of tough to tell a scruff the big mistake he's making."

4. "I sit alone and watch your lights, my only friend through teenage nights, and everything I had to know, I heard it on my radio."

5. "If everybody had a notion across the USA, then everybody'd be surfin' like California, you'll see them wearing their baggies, their roxy sandals too, and bushy bushy blond hairdos".

6. "It's so dark, it's so lonely on the other side from you. I pine a lot, I find a lot falls through without you. I'm

7. "I'm not home right now, but if you want to leave a message, just start talking at the sound of the tone. Hallo, this is your mother. Are you there? Are you coming home?"

8. "Sounded sad upon the radio, broke a million hearts in mono, our mothers cried and sang along, and who'd blame them."

Section 2 60s Classics

1. Who sang "Simon Says"? Was it:
   a) Creedence Clearwater Revival,
   b) The Move,
   c) The 1910 Fruit Gum Co.?

2. "A part of me knows I'm not really living, a butterfly child, so free and so wild and so full of living." Which 60s classic are these lines from?
   a) "Jennifer Eccles" — The Hollies,
   b) "Jezebel" — Marty Wilde,
   c) "Jesamine" — The Casuals?

3. UB40 and Chrissie Hynde went to No. 1 with "I Got You, Babe" in 1985. But what year was it a hit for Sonny and Cher?

4. John Fred and the Playboy Band had a hit with which of these songs?
   a) "Judy in Disguise (With Glasses)"
   b) "Judy says (Knock You In The Head)",
   c) "Judy Teen"?

5. The band which recorded "Riders On The Storm" also had a hit with "Hello I Love You." Who were they?

6. Was the classic Beatles track "Hey Jude" released before or after "Lady Madonna"?

7. "The Leader Of The Pack" was a hit for:
a) The Chiffons,
b) The Shangri-Las,
c) The Shirelles?

8. ". . . cos her hair glows like the sun and her eyes they light the skies." Do these lyrics come from:
a) "DooWah Diddy" — Manfred Mann,
b) "Pretty Flamingo" — Manfred Mann,
c) "Mighty Quinn" — Manfred Mann?

Section 3 Band Names

1. Which band had hits with "Girls' School", "Band on the Run" and "Jet"?

2. Who had a hit with "Classic" in 1982?

3. Who recorded the classic track "Sometimes When We Touch"?

4. Name the band who in 1982 had a hit with the song which included the line:
'Taumatawhakatangihangakoauauota-nateaturipukakapikimaungahoronuku-pokaiwhenuakitanatahu'?

5. Who sang "Happy Birthday Sweet 16"?

6. Name the male duo who recorded "You've Lost That Loving Feeling" in 1965.

7. Name the vocalist who had hits with "Bang Bang", "Knocked it Off" and "Kool in the Kaftan."

Section 4 70s Classics

1. What record gave Cliff Richard his first No. 1 since "Congratulations"?

2. How many ways to leave your lover did Paul Simon come up with in 1976?

3. "They sit at the same table every night at the Mexican discotheque, she gives him French kisses, he gives her French cigarettes." Which hit song do these lines come from?

4. Who sang about kissin' in the back row of the movies in 1974?

5. In which year did Don McLean spend 3 weeks at No. 2 with "American Pie"?

6. "I never thought it would happen, with me and the girl from Clapham out on a windy common, that night I ain't forgotten." Which hit did these lyrics come from?

7. Who was a rocket man in 1972?

8. The Strawbs boasted in 1973 that "You can't get me . . ." — why not?

9. Name Sad Cafe's classic hit which reached No. 3 in 1979.

Section 5 That Was Then . . .

1. Name the singer who recorded "Beautiful Boy" who was previously with the band which recorded "Yesterday".

2. Captain Sensible reached No. 1 in 1982 with "Happy Talk". But which band was he with to record "Love Song" and "New Rose"?

3. When Julian Cope was with The Teardrop Explodes, he recorded such classics as "Treason" and "Colours Fly Away". But was his first solo single called:
a) Sunspots,
b) Sunday Girl,
c) Sunshine Playroom?

4. Name the singer with Genesis who left and recorded "Games Without Frontiers".

5. When the singer mentioned in Q4 left Genesis, the drummer took his place. Name the drummer and his first solo album.

6. Bowie and Jagger reached No. 1 in 1985 with "Dancin' in the Street". But was the Rolling Stones first No. 1:
a) Little Red Rooster,
b) It's All Over Now,
c) (Can't Get No) Satisfaction?

7. Smokey Robinson and the Miracles recorded such classic Motown tracks as "Going to a Go-go" and "Tracks of my Tears". But name his No. 1 hit of 1981.

8. The Skids had hits with such brilliant tracks as "Charade" and "Animation". Name the guitarist with the band, and the group he subsequently formed.

Section 6 80s Classics

1. Name the band who had a hit with "Free Nelson Mandela" in 1984.

2. Yazoo had hits with "Nobody's Diary" and "Only You." But name Alison Moyet's first solo single.

3. Which classic single do these lines come from:
"Well I ought to leave here,
"The rain it never stops and it seems there's something I should know"?

Cont on page 57.

53

BECAUSE I'M BORED, CAROLE! ALL THE EXCITEMENT'S GONE OUT OF THINGS. I FEEL TRAPPED. I WANT TO BE FREE! CAN'T YOU UNDERSTAND?

I MIGHT'VE UNDERSTOOD IF HE'D MET SOMEONE ELSE. MAYBE I WOULD'VE FOUGHT TO WIN HIM BACK. BUT I-I CAN'T FIGHT THIS!

Through a haze she saw the jeweller's shop.

OH — GRANDAD'S WATCH. THE BOY SAID TO COME BACK THIS AFTERNOON.

But . . .

I'M SORRY. MR MOREN SAYS IT'S TOO OLD. HE CAN'T GET THE PART TO FIX IT WITH.

BUT HE MUST BE ABLE TO REPAIR IT — HE MUST!

Carole burst into tears.

I-I'M SORRY. I-I'M BEING STUPID.

NO, YOU'RE NOT. IT MUST MEAN AN AWFUL LOT TO YOU.

IT'S NOT JUST THE WATCH. IT'S — IT'S . . .

But she couldn't go on.

YOU CAN'T LEAVE IN THIS STATE. COME INTO THE BACK SHOP. I'LL MAKE US A COFFEE.

By the time he did, Carole had managed to pull herself together.

THERE. THAT'LL MAKE YOU FEEL BETTER.

I REALLY AM SORRY. YOU MUST THINK ME AN AWFUL FOOL.

NO, I DON'T. THERE'S OBVIOUSLY MORE TO IT THAN A BROKEN WATCH.

Somehow she knew he'd understand.

WOULD YOU BELIEVE — A BROKEN ROMANCE?

SURE! I'VE BEEN THROUGH IT MYSELF.

He sounded slightly bitter.

BUT YOU DO GET OVER IT, I PROMISE YOU. I HAVE.

55

4. Which Stranglers hit was about the effects of whisky?

5. Siouxsie and the Banshees had hits with songs like "Hong Kong Garden" and "Israel". But Siouxsie and Budgie formed The Creatures. Name their first hit.

6. "It didn't hurt me to see how deep the bullet lies, unaware I'm tearing you asunder, there is thunder in our hearts." Which song are these lyrics from?

7. Which band had a hit with "Once in a Lifetime"?

8. Name the No. 2 hit which included the lyrics "The man in the dark in the picture frame, so mystic and soulful"?

9. Name the band who had a hit with a cover of a Dusty Springfield song.

10. Name the duo who got to No. 2 in 1981 with "Endless Love".

continued from page 26

Measure as accurately as you can, but don't get in a panic about it. Near enough will do — the top is in one size to fit any shape and a few small variations won't matter. But do make sure you draw the underarm seam and neckline in a nice curve — as smooth as you can make it.
Now cut it out along the solid lines.

2. Fold your material in half horizontally, selvedges together, then in half again, vertically (like a book). You will have 4 thicknesses of material, like this:-

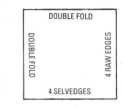

3. Carefully pin on and cut round your pattern, like this:-

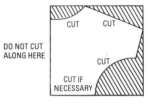

(If you have used 112 cm. wide fabric it will fit exactly — if you've used a wider one there will be some excess fabric at the bottom. Just cut it off.)

4. Take off the pattern and open out the two pieces you will have cut. Lay them one on top of the other, right sides together, and sew, allowing approximately 1.5 cm. seams, like this:-

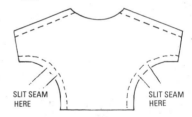

Then with sharp scissors make two slits, about ¾ of the way into the underarm seam, where shown. (This helps the seam lie flat.)

5. Now turn the top right side out and hem the neckline with bias binding. If you haven't used this before don't worry. It's very easy.
You'll see that the bias binding has two edges that have been firmly pressed down.
Open out one of these edges, and starting in the middle of the back neckline (choose whichever side you want for the back — they're both the same), match and sew the edge of the bias binding to the edge of the neckline all the way round, using the creased line on the bias binding as a guide.
When you get back to where you started overlap the binding by 1 cm. cut off any remainder, then finish off firmly. Then turn the bias binding to the inside of your top and sew down firmly. Easy, wasn't it?

6. Now turn up and sew a 1 cm. hem on each sleeve and round the bottom and that's it.
Finished.

And now you've made one, make some more! Cut out the basic shape, and this time cut the back into a V — or the front — or both . . . or why not cut the back lower than the front or vice versa . . . ? It's up to you!

ANSWERS

Section 1 Answers
1. "Cool for Cats" Squeeze.
2. "Reward" The Teardrop Explodes.
3. "Stand and Deliver" Adam and the Ants.
4. "Radio Gaga" Queen.
5. "Surfin' USA" Beach Boys.
6. "Wuthering Heights" Kate Bush.
7. "O Superman" Laurie Anderson.
8. "Come On Eileen" Dexys Midnight Runners.
9. "Rebel Rebel" David Bowie.
10. "Your Song" Elton John.

Section 2 Answers
1. c) The 1910 Fruit Gum Co.
2. c) "Jesamine" The Casuals.
3. It got to No. 1 in August 1965.
4. a) "Jesamine in Disguise (With Glasses)".
5. The Doors.
6. After. "Lady Madonna" was released in March 1968 and "Hey Jude" was released in September 1968.
7. b) The Shangri-Las.
8. b) "Pretty Flamingo".

Section 3 Answers
1. Paul McCartney and Wings.
2. Adrian Gurvitz.
3. Dan Hill.
4. Quantum Jump.
5. Neil Sedaka.
6. The Righteous Brothers.
7. B.A. Robertson.

Section 4 Answers
1. "We Don't Talk Anymore" in 1979.
2. 50.
3. "Moonlighting" Leo Sayer.
4. The Drifters.
5. 1972.
6. "Up the Junction" Squeeze.
7. Elton John.
8. They were "Part of the Union".
9. "Every Day Hurts".

Section 5 Answers
1. John Lennon.
2. The Damned.
3. c) Sunshine Playroom.
4. Peter Gabriel.
5. Phil Collins, "Face Value".
6. b) It's All Over Now.
7. "Being With You".
8. Stuart Adamson, Big Country.

Section 6 Answers
1. Special AKA.
2. "Love Resurrection".
3. "Ghosts", Japan.
4. "Golden Brown".
5. "Miss the Girl".
6. "Running Up That Hill" Kate Bush.
7. Talking Heads.
8. "Vienna" Ultravox.
9. The Tourists.
10. Lionel Richie and Diana Ross.

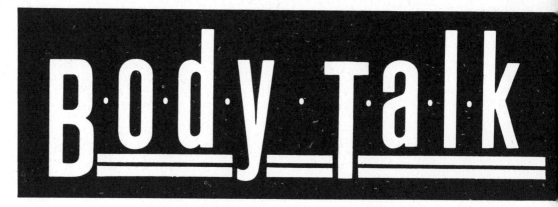

Body Talk

A selection of some of the more common problems from our beauty postbag.

Even though I go to bed fairly early, I still have dark circles under my eyes. What causes them and how can I cover them up?

Lisa, Chester.

Dark circles can be caused by lots of things — lack of sleep, depression, general ill-health, periods and smoking.

The best way to cover them is to apply loads of moisturiser under your eyes, then put on your usual shade of foundation with a sponge, to give a smooth finish.

Next, apply a lighter shade of foundation just *under* the dark circles, along the line they follow. Blend well in and apply loose powder, brushing off any excess with a large brush.

I have lots of tiny white spots around my nose, the corners of my mouth and under my eyes. They're just under the skin and no amount of cleansing and toning gets rid of them. What can I do?

Pamela, Porthcawl.

These 'spots' you describe are actually whiteheads, which form when oil gets trapped in sweat glands.

The only way to get rid of the stubborn ones is to prick them with a sterilised needle and gently squeeze them. Splash your face with cold water, wipe over the area with a toner and use an antiseptic cream to stop infection.

I use mascara every day, but my mum told me it would make my eyelashes fall out. I didn't believe her, but I've noticed a few falling out when I take off my make-up at night. Is the mascara causing this?

Tracy, Harrogate.

No, mascara doesn't make your eyelashes fall out. It's perfectly natural for a few lashes to fall out every day, and they'll probably come loose when you're touching your eyelashes — applying or removing mascara, for example, although

it can also happen while you're washing or rubbing your eyes.

So carry on using mascara and don't worry — it won't harm your eyelashes at all.

I have large, noticeable pores on my nose and chin, but not anywhere else. Is there any way I can get rid of them, or am I stuck with them for life?

Marianne, Bedford.

You can get rid of these open pores, but it could take a few weeks.

Always cleanse your skin thoroughly, using a cleanser for oily skin on the large pores, followed by an astringent toner. Twice weekly use of an exfoliating product like Aapri or The Body Shop's Honey and Oatmeal Scrub Mask will smooth the skin and improve it's appearance.

Stick to this skincare routine and you'll soon notice a difference.

At the moment, my hair is cut in to a bob. I really like it, because it's easy to keep, but I know it's a bit boring. What can I

do to liven it up? I wouldn't mind having it dyed — it's mid-brown, naturally.

Chantal, London.

What about this style by Henry Oakley at the Hair and Beauty Salon, Harrods? The bob is very short at the back, getting longer towards the front with a very short fringe.

The model's hair was fairly dark naturally, but the colour was deepened with L'Oreal's Crescendo colourant for extra impact. Crescendo is permanent and is available at all L'Oreal Hair Technology Salons.

I've got about six or seven different shades of foundation in a drawer — and none of them match my skin. I just can't seem to find one that's exactly right. They're all either too pink or too yellow. My skin is very fair.

Heather, Johnstone.

The first thing you should do is stand in

matter whether your skin is sensitive or not.

However, luckily for you, Almay, who specialise in skincare products and make-up for sensitive skin, recently launched a range of hypo-allergenic tanning products. All products in the range are lanolin and fragrance-free, so can be used even on the most sensitive skin. Prices range from £1.95 to £5.25.

My boyfriend's hair is very short at the back and sides and quite a bit longer on top. He always just washes it and leaves

front of a mirror in broad daylight and take a good look at the natural shade of your skin.

A fair skin needs an ivory shade or a very light shade, like Boots No. 7 Natural Blonde or Almay's Soft Porcelain. Roc have a wide range of colours too.

If, after asking the advice of the beauty consultants in your local department store, you still can't get a light enough shade, Chanel do a pure white shade, specially designed to mix with your normal foundation to get exactly the colour you need. Called Blanc de Chanel, it costs around £14, but will last for ages, as you'll only need a tiny drop at a time.

My skin is really sensitive and I'm allergic to loads of different brands of make-up and skincare products.

This winter, I'm going on holiday to Barbados and because it's so hot there, I'll definitely need a suntan lotion. Only problem is, I'm allergic to that, too! Could I possibly go without it?

Jacqueline, Inverness.

No, you couldn't do without a suntan lotion. In temperatures like the ones in Barbados (even in winter) it's essential to have some protection from the sun, no

it, though, and it looks really boring.

Julie, Hayes.

Probably the best way for your boyfriend to liven his hair up a bit is to use gel to give more height on top.

The model in our photograph is using Wella's High Hair Wet Gel, available from leading hairdressing salons, which gives a really firm hold.

After washing his hair, your boyfriend should towel dry it, then work the gel through his hair with his fingers. He should use more gel, the spikier he wants it to be. Then, he should blow dry his hair, using his fingers to lift the hair up in to spikes.

59

PATCHES

GEORGE MICHAEL

ANDREW RIDGELEY

Looking For A Sign?

Patches charts your year for you!

ARIES (March 21-April 20)

LIFE: Your year begins quietly, with plenty of time to relax after the hectic rush of Christmas. Your calming influence will rub off on your friends who will be grateful for your help. They won't hesitate in coming to your aid later in the year, either!

HIGH SPOTS: From late September to mid December. You'll definitely sparkle in November!

LOW SPOTS: Don't be scared to lean on your friends between early May and mid June — you'll need them.

ROMANCE: Well starred, but be prepared for slight setbacks in August.

'87 changes: The year to do something different. Go hiking, or pony-trekking; make sure it's something you've never done before. Biggest changes are likely around early July.

TAURUS (April 21-May 20)

LIFE: Some slight upsets at the beginning of the year, but the support and advice from a person you had never thought of as a friend before will help you through, and result in a gradually strengthening friendship. This will also bring lots of laughs!

HIGH SPOTS: From late June to early September, you'll feel on top of the world. August looks like being a non-stop whirl of exciting events.

LOW SPOTS: Late November to mid December, but it won't be that bad — honest!

ROMANCE: Someone special enters your life in the summertime.

'87 changes: Changes will happen gradually although you may feel that things are standing still. When you look back at the end of the year, though, you'll realise how much has happened!

GEMINI (May 21-June 20)

LIFE: A promising start to the year, with encouragement from all sides. Don't let your hopes run too high, though, as something unexpected may bring you down to earth with a bump!

HIGH SPOTS: Late October to mid December shows a time of great progress and is full of opportunities.

LOW SPOTS: Late May to early June may be a frustrating time, with your plans being called to a temporary standstill.

ROMANCE: Lots of new people will enter your life this year. And that someone special might just be among them!

'87 changes: There may not be any major changes in your life this year, but you'll be directly affected by the changes in the lives of others.

CANCER (June 21-July 21)

LIFE: You'll feel a great sense of contentment, with your ambitions seemingly fulfilled, but you may begin to feel slightly isolated and long to meet new people.

HIGH SPOTS: The very beginning of the year until mid March shows that someone up there likes you!

LOW SPOTS: From early November to mid December you may experience a different side of life.

ROMANCE: Slight disharmony in your personal life, but your family are a great source of support.

'87 changes: Changes may be slightly unwelcome and definitely unexpected, but on reflection you'll see that you benefited from them in the long run!

LEO (July 22-August 21)

LIFE: Bad experiences at the end of 1986 may have left you with rather bitter feelings about certain aspects of your life, but you will become more enthusiastic about the coming year when your friends catch you up in their plans!

HIGH SPOTS: Early April to late June will be a time of rapid progress.

LOW SPOTS: The progress will slow down and almost come to a halt between late September and early November.

ROMANCE: July could be hotter than hot this year!

'87 changes: Changes will be chiefly in your attitude this year. Don't lose touch with friends, though.

VIRGO (August 22-September 21)

LIFE: A strange lack of enthusiasm is evident at the beginning of 1987, but an early jolt throws you into a new project which brings you into contact with lots of different people. Make the most of it!

HIGH SPOTS: You'll remember the events of early June to mid August with fondness.

LOW SPOTS: Mid January to late February may be better forgotten.

ROMANCE: A holiday romance will haunt you for a LONG time!

'87 changes: Have you considered taking up an interest which lets you express yourself freely? Amateur dramatics can be a great laugh, and may well lead to something bigger!

LIBRA (September 22-October 22)

LIFE: A strange start to 1987, but you'll soon sort out the confusion and find your feet. The year progresses steadily, but ends with you in a rather subdued mood. Don't worry — all the excitement at Christmas will snap you out of that!

HIGH SPOTS: An unforgettable time between mid August and mid October.

LOW SPOTS: You may feel that the

weeks between early March and mid April will never come to an end!

ROMANCE: Your wandering spirit will want to take you off to the islands, and (if you get there!) there may be an island boy for you!

'87 changes: You'll become more settled. The changes in your life may seem to be a bit overwhelming, but your Libran level head should soon balance them out!

SCORPIO (October 23-November 21)

LIFE: This year sees Scorpio in a supremely confident mood! Don't raise your hopes *too* high, but your confidence should pay off and leave you feeling that you can take on the world.

HIGH SPOTS: Late September to mid November will be a time of great progress in your career.

LOW SPOTS: The high spots will outweigh the slight disappointments of mid March to early May.

ROMANCE: You may feel that you've no time for love this year — things are moving too fast as it is!

'87 changes: You'll become more health-conscious this year, and that includes early nights and a healthy diet. Try to count to ten from now on before blowing your top!

SAGITTARIUS (November 22-December 21)

LIFE: You may feel that you'll never find your feet this year, but don't despair, you'll find someone who'll only be too glad to help! By Spring you'll feel a little more

stable — and the year will run smoothly!

HIGH SPOTS: Mid October to late November means progress for your long-term plans.

LOW SPOTS: There are a couple of setbacks during November, though . . .

ROMANCE: There are few bumps on the road to happiness!

'87 changes: A year when you discover your TRUE friends! Don't forget to include your family in your plans and dreams.

CAPRICORN (December 22-January 19)

LIFE: Enthusiasm oozes from every pore at the beginning of 1987, but make sure your friends and family fall in with your plans!

HIGH SPOTS: Your hard work will be well rewarded between mid August and early October!

LOW SPOTS: Early March to late April seems to drag . . .

ROMANCE: One of the highlights of the year — you'll meet someone VERY special.

'87 changes: Something may happen to

change your life completely, and those changes continue right into the new year!

AQUARIUS (January 20-February 18)

LIFE: The year begins with a steady continuation of the progress made at the end of 1986. Don't be disheartened, however, if it seems that what you plan is being called to a halt by someone who has nothing to do with the situation. Any unforeseen circumstances will be explained in the fullness of time, and the year will end in a fairly contented mood with nothing to do but sit back and enjoy the Christmas season.

HIGH SPOTS: Late September to the end of the year!

LOW SPOTS: May is a fairly dull time!

ROMANCE: Any worries are quickly forgotten when a new boy appears in your life.

'87 changes: You'll begin to plan ahead instead of acting on impulse. You'll learn your lesson after a time of sudden upheaval!

PISCES (February 19-March 20)

LIFE: You could quite easily find yourself in a position of responsibility at the beginning of 1987. This makes you feel important but rather uncomfortable at the same time. This dominant position will gradually diminish and this will give you the opportunity to sit back and watch others doing all the work. The end of the year will bring rewards for your earlier hard work.

HIGH SPOTS: Early November to the end of the year will be happy — but VERY busy!

LOW SPOTS: Try to take a break between early March and mid April — you'll need it!

ROMANCE: You may find it difficult to be pleasant at times, but SOMEONE will bring out the best in you!

You'll be slightly confused by a friend's loyalties and this may lead you to take a closer look at your life!

1. The pressure's on . . .

Prefab Sprout wonder why the audience haven't turned up (hasn't anyone told them that there's *never* an audience at 'Whistle Test'?), and get ready to do their stuff on live T.V.

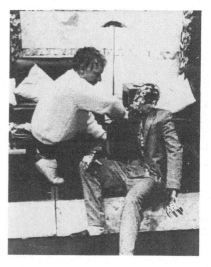

2. Richard Skinner chants his way through this week's charts while the 'Whistle Test' silver man complains that he can't read the autocue.

3. Someone finds a board with 'Skilly-Pot' (?) written on it, so Andy decides to hold it in front of the camera while he's on screen (just for a bit of a larf . . .).

4. "Are you OK? Not nervous? You can see the autocue now? Not nervous? Remembered to polish your head and demagnetise your teeth?"

A concerned 'Whistle Test' person gives the silver man (the star of the show) V.I.P. treatment and makes sure he won't fluff his lines . . .

WHISTLE BLOWS

Ever wondered what goes on behind the scenes at a live T.V. show? PATCHES reveals all as we visit 'Whistle Test' at B.B.C. T.V. Centre . . .

5. The Andy Kershaw Fan Club on their annual outing to the 'Whistle Test' studio stand and gape in awe as their hero does his stuff . . .

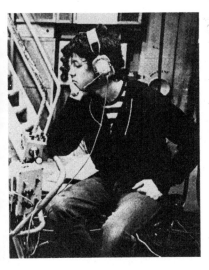

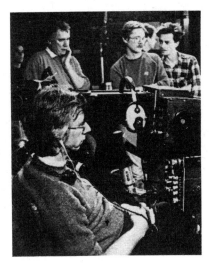

6. "Wow, this week's show's really riveting! Oh, they've put a video on. Gives me just enough time to check out this new Iron Maiden album I bought today . . ."
Confessions of a T.V. soundman.

7. Mark Ellen proving that he's a real T.V. presenter by showing that thing they all stick in their back pocket with a wire attached to an earpiece (or is it simply just a hearing-aid? After all, he is getting on a bit . . .).

8. How come all T.V. crews always look so worried/bored/tired? Another show over and it's smiles all round . . .

STAGE STRUCK

All I'd ever wanted to do was study drama and dancing, but now there were more important things on my mind . . .

WE are therefore happy to inform you that you have been accepted as a student of Theatre and Drama . . ."

I read the letter again, for the twentieth time. I should have been over the moon with the news, because all I'd ever wanted to do was study drama and dancing, but somehow it had all managed to go wrong.

When I'd found out that I'd been accepted, I was ecstatic. I phoned my best friend Carol straight away, and we laughed and planned and talked for ages, and she seemed as happy as I was.

There was only one problem. My boyfriend, Jamie, didn't know I'd even applied for Drama School, let alone been accepted. I knew he would feel hurt that I hadn't mentioned it to him, but I reckoned that there was no point in upsetting him if I wasn't going to get in. If I failed the audition, Jamie need never know anything about it.

I didn't fail the audition, though, and now Jamie had to be told. He would probably have several fits to begin with, but once he'd calmed down, he would see that nothing really had to change. The college was only twenty miles away, and we would see each other at weekends. Come to think of it, that's about the only time we saw each other anyway, what with his football and my drama club.

I'd been all ready to break it to him gently that evening but Carol had beaten me to it. Jamie turned up at my house, upset, offended and flaming mad. I tried to explain, but he just wouldn't listen, and in the end he stormed off in a temper.

I looked up from my letter at Carol, who was standing by my bedroom window. "What did you have to go and tell him for?" I burst out suddenly. "Everything was going OK until you messed it up."

Carol turned from the window and frowned before she moved over to my stereo.

"You should have told him right at the beginning," she said. "No wonder he thought you were deceiving him."

"You *know* why I didn't tell him then," I snapped in exasperation. "It would have all worked out fine if you'd kept out of it." I couldn't help it, I started crying again.

Carol sighed impatiently, and I nearly choked myself trying to shut up. I don't know what it was about Carol, but she always made me feel so childish. She made me feel that losing a boyfriend you really care about was no reason to start crying.

"Well," she said smoothly, getting up to leave, "it's probably the best thing that could have happened. I mean, from what Jamie was saying, you've been on the verge of breaking up for some time."

And she walked out, leaving me in floods of tears and sick with shock.

The Drama School hardly mattered now I'd lost Jamie.

So Jamie had been thinking about a split for a while! Did that mean he'd been seeing someone else in the meantime? Had he just been looking for an excuse to get rid of me? Suddenly I felt more miserable than ever. The Drama School hardly mattered now that I'd lost Jamie.

Thinking back on it, I suppose things had started to change when I'd been offered the lead in the school play. I'd spent a lot of time in rehearsals, or practising my songs or dances, but Jamie seemed to understand. Had he found another girl while I'd been busy? When the show opened, I'd had very good notices, and Jamie had seemed very pleased. But Carol had told me he was glad when it was all over.

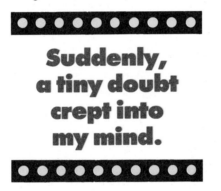

Suddenly, a tiny doubt crept into my mind.

Then I'd joined the local drama group, and Jamie had said he was worried that the plays were becoming more important than him.

"It's just that we don't seem to be seeing very much of each other these days," he'd explained. "Even Carol noticed — she asked if everything was OK between us."

Suddenly, a tiny doubt crept into my mind. Carol had had rather too much to do with Jamie and I. I'd never noticed it before, but things seemed to be falling into place now. Quite simply, she was jealous of us, and had been trying to split us up.

I stood up and grabbed my coat, ready to go round to her house and sort things out, but just as I reached the front door, the bell rang.

I opened the door slowly, expecting Carol and ready to blow

her head off with a mouthful of abuse. In fact it was Jamie, and the surprise left me standing with my chin on the carpet.

"Kim," he ventured, his eyes on his feet, "I just came round to say I'm sorry for cracking up like that. I mean, I know you've been thinking of splitting up for a while, but I'd like to talk to you about it first."

"And Carol told you that, right?" I said resignedly. "Just do me a favour, Jamie, and forget every word Carol's ever said to you."

Jamie grinned, suddenly hopeful. "Fair enough."

He came in, and we talked things over. Just the way I'd planned in the first place.

"I want to see you do well, Kim," he told me. "Of course I do. It's just that you'll meet other guys who know more about acting and are more interested in it than I am . . ."

I looked at his uncertain expression and felt like laughing and crying all at once, even though I knew that Carol had put all these nasty little ideas in his head.

"Don't be a prawn, Jamie," I said. "If I thought that was going to happen I'd finish with you now."

A quick grin lit up his face, and he jumped up and grabbed his coat.

"Come on, let's go and tell my mum the good news."

Happily, I followed him out.

Halfway down the road, we bumped into Carol, and the usual welcoming smile didn't appear on Jamie's face.

"Hey, Carol," he called, "your mate's going to be a star! D'you want her autograph now, while there's still no charge?"

I knew then that he really was proud of me, and that we wouldn't ever be split up again by any nasty-minded gossip.

Carol knew too, and she walked on without a word.

RIGHT now, you're probably falling out with your family more than ever before. If you've got brothers and sisters, you may not notice much difference — punch-ups over the black eyeliner and other such important issues, or belting your brother round the ear for playing football with your teddy in front of your new boyfriend, not to mention calling *him* Kevin when his name's Geoff — nothing unusual.

But perhaps you're finding that falling out with your parents, and your mum especially, is the easiest thing in the world. That's because you're growing up — *grown* up — and she won't admit it! She won't admit that you're almost an adult now, she disapproves of your clothes and boyfriends automatically, she nags on at you about pathetic things like keeping your room in order — I mean, what does it matter what disgusting diseases are breeding in the half empty coffee cup under your bed when you could be hanging out the window looking at sexy Steve next door?

Well, hold it right there. Let's consider this problem from your mum's point of view, which is, after all, the quickest way to make things better for you!

Housework and Freedom

The reason these two are together is because, indirectly, they are related. I can almost hear you saying "Yeah — one prevents the other," but this isn't the case!

Look at it this way. You want to be treated like an adult, be allowed out to whatever time you like, and be allowed to wear what you want. You know you're sensible, and that you can look after yourself.

Fair enough. Nothing wrong with that . . . but let's see how your mum sees it. What does she see in her beloved daughter that merits such treatment? She sees you scrapping with your sister over make-up, she sees you sulking when you don't get your own way, she sees you blowing all your pocket money on a George Michael poster, then grubbing off your dad for the rest of the week, and she sees you dicing with death, hanging out of the window by one tooth and three toenails in the hope of catching a glimpse of Steve next door. Good sound evidence for treating you like an adult? We think not!

Like it or not, being an adult means that you're a responsible person, not that you can stay out late or date anyone you like. So arguing and sulking won't get you anywhere — but try hanging up your clothes when you come in, or making the bed occasionally, or vacuuming the house without being asked. That should do wonders!

I mean, after all, your mother's under no contract to run about tidying up after you when you can't be bothered, is she? So talk to her about it. Remember, she still thinks of you as her little girl, even although you're not, and let's face it, we are living in a pretty dangerous world. Be prepared to tell your mum where you're going, who with, and how you're getting back. Promise to phone if you're delayed. If she sees no risk to your safety in the plan, there shouldn't be any

problem, 'cos she does have your best interests at heart, after all!

Boyfriends and Clothes

Boyfriends cause the most awful rows between mothers and daughters, and the most common reason is because your mum doesn't think he's good enough for you. But then again, she probably doesn't think any rotten boy's good enough for her daughter! It hasn't occurred to her that you aren't going to marry him, so she's probably over-reacting.

Unless your boyfriend really is a bad influence on you, your mum's probably not justified in saying some of the things

IS YOUR MOTHER SUPERIOR?

she does, so the best thing to do is talk it over with her; tell her all his good points — being careful, however, to omit mentioning his sexy eyes and his hairy chest, as we don't reckon that this is likely to impress.

However, another thing to remember is that your mum went out with boys too — and she probably knows what type of a guy he is after a couple of meetings.

She can tell from experience if he's the sneaky type or if he's using you, and because you're her daughter, she doesn't like it. But you'll just have to explain that discovering what sort of a person your boyfriend is is something you'll have to do by yourself. And if he does turn out to be a two-timing rat — you'll just have to hope Mum won't say I told you so!

So there you are, all dolled up ready

to go to the disco. You step into the living-room to say goodbye, and what happens? Your mother screams and collapses on the floor. Sound familiar? What, you say to yourself, puzzled, is wrong with her? It couldn't be you, could it? But there's nothing about a leather mini, green rinsed hair, biker's jacket, fishnet tights and nine inch stillettos that would make someone faint, is there?

Well, maybe not as far as you and your mates are concerned. But in your mum's day, dressing like that hadn't even been thought of at fancy dress parties! Your mum really can't understand why anyone would want to look like that in the first place! Well,

how you dress is really your own affair, but you could try to show a little consideration too. We know that it's the person underneath the cemented make-up that counts, so try to explain that. And *don't* go out of your way to dress obnoxiously — compromise a little!

Remember that communication is all important in a relationship, especially with your mother. If you need her advice, ask for it. If she's in a bad mood, ask her why. Always try to be as considerate as possible, especially just now, because things have changed and you're growing up. You're not your mum's little girl any more and she has to have time to get used to it. Don't make life miserable for both of you — after all, your mum's the best friend you're ever likely to have — so make sure she knows it!

SECOND TIME AROUND

YOU know how it is, Cedric calls round in the Bentley to ask you to the Garden party up at the manor house. You of course accept, giving no thought to the fact that your old jeans and sweatshirt will cut no ice with the stuck-up lot up at the manor. But you have to go, you're a woman of your word, and besides, you'll get the feed of a lifetime! So here's what to do — beg or borrow a few quid and set off for the second hand shops, and this is what you could come up with . . .

1

Details overleaf . . .

2

3

1 Old dresses are often so fancy that they need very little to dress them up. The blue dress on the previous page cost five pounds from Oxfam, and the intricate neckline means that you don't have to buzz about looking for matching jewellery.

2 For something more formal, black won't go far wrong. These two were from Oxfam and cost between four and six pounds. Look out for unusual beaded dresses, which are usually quite cheap, as they're seldom less than a size sixteen! Just tie it round your middle with a scarf, or run a couple of simple seams down either side.

3 Fifties dance dresses with pleated backs can cover a multitude of sins, or create a few curves on flat surfaces! This one cost £2.50 from a Salvation army shop.

4 "Fancy a quick Charleston, Cedric? Sickly pink number to keep his mum sweet. £3.50 from Oxfam.

5 Shine on with a satin beaded evening dress, but hold on to your chair when you sit down. Slithering under the table is unlikely to impress . . .

6 Another shiner, this one, with material success for shoulder-rubbers. £5 from the Old Peoples Welfare Shop.

4

5

6

THE ROSEGARDEN

June 28 1886

Dear Diary,

I thank Heaven for you tonight for I swear I would go mad, could I not speak of what is in my heart. There is no-one to whom I may speak of my feelings, no-one who has listened to my hopes and dreams and fears and guarded all my secrets since first I learned to write of them. And now, I must burden you with the heaviest secret of all. What I say will come as no surprise to you. It will be only my last few words on a subject which has so occupied my mind and my heart these past months that I have spoken to you of little else.

Oh, you must be sick to death of my tears and complaints — but now, I know that you will forgive me for you know that only when I am alone can I speak of it at all. With everyone else, with my sisters and my friends, even with dear Mama, I must smile and laugh and talk of parties and visits and tapestries and Mrs Leighton's hat and Abigail's new poodle and of what colour we shall make the new drawing-room curtains, as if it mattered, as if anything mattered anymore. Yet, they must never guess . . . Only when I'm alone can I say, "My heart is breaking."

Oh no, I must not say that — it is foolish of me to be so distraught for, of course, I have known for a long time now that it must come to this, that Mr Townsley must someday declare his love for my dear friend Isabella . . . is it not the very thing for which I myself have been striving since first she told me of her love for our handsome new friend?

Have I not made every effort to throw them in each other's way, to ensure that they should miss no chance to talk to one another, and to be alone together for a few brief moments away from the watchful eyes of our families and friends? Was it not I who carried messages from one to another so that no-one should know of their love before they were sure of it themselves? And have I not always been the one to comfort and reassure when foolish doubts arose — there was no need for doubt. I always knew . . . because I watched for the swift, sidelong glance, the particular smile which speaks of love when no words may be uttered — and did I not weep when I saw them!

Isabella is my dearest friend, the sweetest and kindest girl, and truly, you must believe me, I wish her well. I wish her all the happiness in the world, and now I know that she will find it. She deserved the very best, and now she has it . . .

Forgive my tears. It is only for tonight and then I will not speak of it again . . . Oh but, why, *why* did it have to be him? Why did she, whom I love as a sister, have to give her heart to the one man who has ever captured mine?

On his very first call here, the most formal of visits, made simply to introduce himself to his new neighbours, I saw his face and knew than I loved him . . . and later, of course, we all became friends . . . Then Isabella told me that she loved him and that if she did not win his love she must surely go into a decline, and would I not help her — I, her dearest, dearest friend — all this knowing nothing of how I felt for the gentleman of whom we spoke — and what could I do but say "Yes"?

And now, this evening, here in my own house at the little party which Papa promised that I and my sisters might hold for our friends, Mr Townsley and Isabella announced their betrothal.

There is nothing, I am sure, which can prepare one for a blow such as that. I have known for so long that the moment must eventually come and even so as I saw them standing there, smiling and holding hands and receiving the congratulations of all our friends, I thought I must surely cry out, "No! No! No!" But I did not, of course . . . Instead, I smiled and clapped and drank their health and even kissed them both and cried a little for the joy of it all — or so they thought . . . Then, as the dancing started, I slipped out into the garden and away down the path between the trees to the little rose garden where I might be alone to sit and weep, away from the heartbreak of the merriment indoors.

It was warm and light still, with all the grass and the flowers sparkling and glistening after a shower of rain, and there were so many colours — crimson and gold and peach, pink as pale as the dawn and white as rich and pure and creamy as a wedding-gown. I sat for a little while on the stone seat by the stream, closing my eyes and letting the water soothe my aching heart with its gentle murmurings. The air was so soft and so full of the scent of roses . . . so beautiful that I thought I would swoon with grief . . .

I did not realise that I was not alone there until I opened my eyes and saw Edmund Mortimer standing at my side and looking most concerned. Dear Edmund — he is so kind. He told me that he had seen me leave the house looking somewhat distressed and had followed to discover whether he could perhaps be of some assistance.

His company did not irk me so much as that of the others — he is all consideration and he asks no questions — although, in the end, when I could hold back the tears no longer, it seemed from things he said that he had already guessed at the reason for my sorrow. I said nothing to confirm his suspicions and he did not press me to speak of it but simply told me, as if it was in some way important, that the roses which are so beautiful this evening will one day wither, and their petals fall, leaving only the thorns to lie black and seemingly dead throughout the winter. But at length, he told me, spring would come, with its sun and gentle showers and, by the summer, there would be new roses . . .

We sat for a little longer and then, my composure regained, thanks to Edmund's kindness and consideration, we returned to the party and I smiled as brightly and danced as gaily in honour of the happy couple as anyone there.

And now it is over and I am alone with you and there need be no more false smiles, no more pretence. William and Isabella will be married at the end of October and I will be happy for them, truly, for they are my dearest friends. I am to be chief bridesmaid. I wonder what flowers one carries to an October wedding. At least it will not be roses. I do not think I will ever again be able to bear the smell of roses . . .

25th October 1886

William and Isabella are married. They looked so happy . . . Isabella carried the most beautiful spray of lilies and we, her attendants, smaller bouquets of the same. Everyone was very merry. Papa drank too much and Mr Townsley's little nephews ran away with the top tier of the wedding cake. They had eaten it all before they were found. Edmund was very kind, as always, and made me dance when I would rather have hidden away. Mama and her friends are all saying now that I must be the next to go. Never! I will not do it. I will not marry a man I could never love simply for the sake of not being left on the shelf!

1st December 1886

I have been neglecting you again. It is extremely cold now and the little pond in the park is quite frozen over. Edmund and some of his friends are coming this afternoon to take us all skating. He is such a good friend and I am glad of his company now that Isabella is so much taken up with her wifely duties. A letter arrived from Grandmama and Grandpapa to say that they will be coming to us for Christmas. It will be lovely to see them.

2nd January 1887

Christmas was lovely with all the family here and all our friends around to visit. Mama and Papa gave me a beautiful gold locket with their portraits inside. I will cherish it always. Edmund is often here and has confessed to a deep regard for me. I wish I could feel the same for him but I do not suppose that I will ever love any but William. Perhaps I should see less of Edmund under the circumstances but it would only hurt him and I enjoy his company so much that I would be loathe to snub him in any way. He will not press me, I know. How lucky I am to have so good a friend.

12th March 1887

William and Isabella are expecting a happy event. If it is a girl, they will call her Emily, after me. It is lovely of them to think of it. Edmund and I have put a swing in the garden for my little sisters but it is such fun that I fear I play with it more than they do!

1st May 1887

Arose at dawn to wash my face in the dew so that I should look my best for the May Ball at the Linton's this evening. What a marvellous party it was. Edmund and I danced until I thought I should drop, and Mrs Higgins, who thinks dancing is a sin, huffed and puffed and glared at us all until she went purple in the face. Then she had the affrontery to ask Mama is she was not ashamed to have reared so abandoned a creature as myself! Dear Mama — she simply told the old crow not to upset herself or she would burst her stays. I felt sure Mrs Higgins must be about to have an apoplexy. Isabella looked radiant as ever. She is very heavy with child. It cannot be long now.

17th June 1887

It's a girl! Little Emily, my namesake, came into the world at a quarter past four this afternoon, a little earlier than expected, but as healthy and jolly and bouncy a baby as anyone could ever wish to see — and every bit as beautiful as her mother. Isabella is very well and everyone is simply overjoyed. I am so happy for them. The christening has already been arranged and I am to be godmother. I must buy a very special present for little Emily. Edmund and I went boating   again this afternoon and I have promised to rise early tomorrow morning and accompany him along with some others of our friends on a fishing expedition. Must go to bed now or I shall look awful in the morning.

There seems barely time even to sleep these days!

2nd July 1887

Summer at last! Edmund brought round some strawberries — my first this year — and we ate them with cream in the garden. He has been strangely quiet these past few days. At little Emily's Christening, I caught him looking at me so oddly that I was moved to ask whether I had in some way hurt or offended him, but he has assured me that this is not the case. I do wish that he would tell me what is wrong. I could not bear it if anything were to come between us . . .

13th July 1887

I think I will die of happiness. I can hardly sit still and even now, as I write this, my heart is dancing with the stars. Oh diary, I can keep it a secret no longer — Edmund has proposed! This evening as we stood talking by the swing, he reached for my hand and led me down the path to the rose-garden. The scent and the colour of the roses brought back such a host of memories that I could not help but smile. Edmund asked me very gently if I did not still find it painful to think of that other evening when we walked there together.

I told him truthfully that I simply found it strange to think how long ago and far away it all seems and then I drew a deep breath and confessed at long last that the only thoughts which the smell of roses bring to me now are those of his kindess on that awful night and of my great love for him which has grown up through the dark and lonely months of winter.

At first, he was so quiet that I thought for one awful moment that I had mistaken his feelings for me, and then all of a sudden he gave a great cry of relief and joy and swept me into his arms and asked me to become his wife.

Mama and Papa shall hear in the morning and I know they will be overjoyed for already they love him as a son. My only sadness is that the wedding will be too late in the year for my bouquet to be of roses. I think that for the rest of my life, I will love nothing so much as the smell of roses.

IN A SPIN!

WE get sackfuls of letters from readers asking for advice about the career they fancy when they leave school.

When Nicky Herridge from London wrote to us asking for advice on how to become a Press Officer for a record company we decided to let her try her hand at it.

A Press Officer's job involves looking after the pop stars on the label to make sure that their photographs, interviews and reviews of their records appear in all the important newspapers and magazines.

Thanks to all at Chrysalis Records Press Office for showing Nicky the ins and outs of their job, and for putting up with us all for a whole day!

1

2

3

4

5

1. Nicky was supposed to start work at ten o'clock and
s already half past ... the first sign that she'll make a
reat Press Officer!
2. Rumour has it that what they put in the tea helps you
et the front door open in the mornings ... Nicky has a
t of bother with it.
3. First thing she has to do is organise a set of
elephone interviews for Alvin Stardust ... not the
asiest task in the world!
4. Midge Ure's just recently done a new photo-session,
nd it's up to Nicky to see that all the right people get
rints of the shots.
5. Filing is the most boring part of a Press Officer's job,
nd guess who's been lumbered with the task today ...
6. Next thing ... typing out a Press release that Nicky's
ritten herself — 'Go West Announce That They've
oth Got Very Big Noses' ... or something along these
nes ...
7. Another caller, ready to talk to Alvin.
8. Doing a mail out. Nicky has to send a copy of each
ew single and album released that week to different
ournalists of various shapes and sizes all over the
ountry.
9. Choosing which shots of new signing 'The Reckless
rannies' (?) to have duplicated and sent out to
veryone.
0. It's getting near six o'clock, and Nicky's finished a
ard day's work. Chrysalis Press Officer Clare Smith
hows her some of the Press cuttings that have come
nto the office over the past few days.
1. Time for home, Nicky wanders through the record
ompany reception on her way to *that door* again!
2. 'Mmmmm ... stars of tomorrow. Mind you, listen to
hat guitarist! On second thoughts, maybe not ...'
3. Still smiling after all that work! Nicky relaxes with a
uppa. "I wish I could do that every day!"

75

T HE F T RE

1

H AVE you ever sat in the hairdressers wondering exactly what was happening behind the closed door of the beauty room?

Well, so have we! None of us was brave enough to go and find out, though, so we sent reader, Phyllis, who's sixteen, to have a full beauty treatment and then let her tell us all about it!

Over to you, Phyllis!

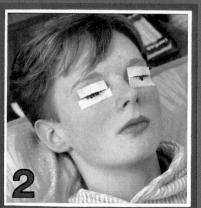

2

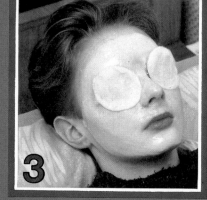

3

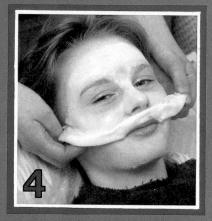

4

5

6

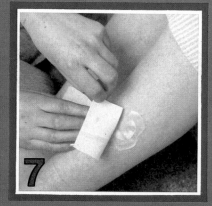

7

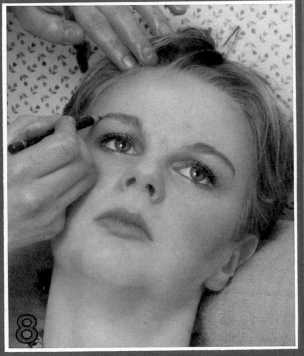

1) "Well, this is me arriving at the salon. I look a bit nervous, don't I? That's because I was!"

2) "This is me having an eyelash tint. Harriet, who was giving me my beauty treatments, explained that it was just like hair dye — a mixture of peroxide to lift my own colour, and a dark brown dye for the new colour.

"It's ideal for people like me with light-coloured lashes, because it dyes them a nice natural shade and lasts for six to eight weeks. So, I don't have to use mascara for a whole six weeks!

"It costs about £3.50, but I think it's well worth it."

3) "This is a paraffin wax beauty treatment. The warm wax is painted on with a brush and left for about twenty minutes. It's supposed to stimulate the circulation and relax the client, but I found it a bit warm for comfort.

"When it was peeled off, though, my face did feel relaxed and very smooth."

4) "The paraffin wax being peeled off. Looks disgusting, doesn't it?" (Yes!)

5) "This is me soaking my nails in warm, soapy water before my manicure.

"After they'd been cleaned and dried, my nails were filed and Harriet used cuticle remover and an orange stick to push back my cuticles.

"Then, they were painted with base coat, two coats of nail varnish and a top coat."

6) "The finished look. It's different, anyway!"

7) "Ughh! I hate this picture. This is a leg wax to remove the hairs from my legs.

"Harriet painted on hot wax with a spatula in the direction the hairs grew, waited until the wax dried and then ripped it off in the opposite direction!

"And yes, it did hurt a bit!"

8) "Now for the make-up. This was great. I felt really pampered — what a luxury!"

9) "This is me at the end of my beauty treatments, feeling great — hope I looked great, too!"

So, did Phyllis think that the beauty treatments had been worthwhile?

"Oh, yes — I had a great day. I'm glad I didn't have to pay for it, though!

"The total cost would have been £37.50, so I couldn't really have afforded it all.

"Although I enjoyed the paraffin wax treatment, it was too expensive for me and so was the leg wax. I'll stick to shaving!

"I thought the eyelash tint was well worth it, though, and I'll definitely have that done again. I loved the make-up, too, because I could never have done it so well myself.

"I had a fantastic day — it was great to feel so pampered. Thanks, Patches!"

In case you're interested in any of these treatments, here are the prices Phyllis would have paid. But remember, prices vary from town to town and salon to salon.

TREATMENT	COST
EYELASH TINT	£3.50
PARAFFIN WAX	£6.00
MANICURE	£7.00
LEG WAX	
UP TO KNEE	£8.00
FULL LEG	£11.00
FACIAL AND MAKE-UP	£10.00

DO the leaves left in the bottom of your tea cup mean anything to you — or are you one of the growing band of tea bag users who don't believe in the old art of tea leaf reading? Well, if you are, you don't know what you're missing! After all, tea leaves have been telling the future for centuries. And you'll probably have to admit that there have been a couple of times in your life when you'd have loved to know what was going to happen next. So why not learn?

You'll be surprised at how quickly and easily you can pick up the tricks of the fortune teller's trade. Start off with a white cup or mug. White is the best colour because it means that you can see the tea leaves more easily. Don't be tempted to cheat and cut open a tea-bag, though. The tea leaves used in everyday bags are smaller and not as good as loose tea which can be bought quite cheaply in your local supermarket. These leaves tend to be larger and darker — not to mention easier to read!

Make your tea in the ordinary way and then pour the tea, don't strain it, into the cups. When the person whose cup you are going to read has finished, they should turn their cup upside down on a saucer or a small plate and turn the cup three times in a clockwise manner. You are then ready to start reading! Don't, whatever you do, read your own cup — this is extremely unlucky.

If, and it happens sometimes, there is barely any sign of tea leaves left in the cup, this means that the person's life is going smoothly and that the person will have luck in the near future.

The nearer the leaves are to the handle or the top of the cup, the sooner the events in the cup are going to happen. The nearer the bottom of the cup, the further away the event.

Don't be afraid to turn the cup around so that you can recognise all the various shapes. We've outlined the most common shapes likely to be found in your tea cup and using our guideline — and a little imagination! — you could be the wow of your next school fete. Madam Zelda watch out!

Separate dots — Money or possessions; their positions indicate when, and how large or small the amount.

Circles — Energy or power to influence events; completion of projects that have been started.

Crosses — A dramatic change.

Wavy or Curved lines — A need for caution, careful thought, intelligent planning and better direction and control.

Groups or cluster — The emotions; their size and position will show the extent of emotional responses to events, and associated patterns will indicate whether happiness or sadness is involved.

An arrow near the top and quite close to the handle means important news will soon arrive.

A ladder suggests sustained effort which will have good results.

A cross indicates a small choice or change some time away depending on how far away from the rim or bottom it is.

A basket means that a welcome arrival is imminent.

A ball suggests restlessness will be experienced soon.

An eye means an important offer will be made which needs careful investigation.

A series of dots from top to bottom means money, and it shows here that the money will come in over a long period, but not yet.

The sun at the bottom of the cup indicates a slight improvement on all fronts coming soon.

A tree shape means your career — the healthier and more complete looking it is, the better things will work out for you.

A broken initial means that the person with that name is confused and unsure of himself — watch out if this is a boyfriend!

A hand is a handshake and a meeting — a pleasant one!

A horse shoe means good luck!

Really it's just a case of using your imagination and seeing things from the shapes of the leaves. Don't be afraid to follow hunches, no matter how daft they sound. You may find that you have a certain instinctive feel for fortune telling! Mind you, if you find out where John Taylor is going to spend his holidays next year you will let us know, won't you . . . ?

A college library in the year 2183.
YOU KNOW WHAT IMPRESSES ME ABOUT THE 20TH CENTURY, MELA? THEY LIVED SUCH ROMANTIC LIVES!
OH? THAT ISN'T WHAT OUR HISTORY PROFESSOR SAYS . . .
Give Love A Chance!
D'YOU KNOW, THEY ACTUALLY HANDLED THE FOOD THEY ATE?
H'MM — VERY UNHYGIENIC, I GRANT YOU. BUT THEY COULD FALL IN LOVE AND MARRY WHO THEY LIKED . . .
HOW SELFISH! OUR MARRIAGE ARRANGEMENT COUNCIL IS A LOT MORE SCIENTIFIC. BETTER FOR EVERYBODY!
NOT FOR JANN AND I . . .
For Trina had a secret— an illegal love-affair.
THIS IS NO GOOD, JANN. YOU'RE TAKING A TERRIBLE RISK EVERY TIME YOU COME TO SEE ME.
I DON'T CARE, TRINA — I LOVE YOU. I WANT TO MARRY YOU!
AND BY SAYING THAT YOU'VE BROKEN THE LAW! IF ANYONE HEARD YOU SAY YOU LOVE ME . . .
I KNOW — I'D BE ELIMINATED UNDER CODE 42 OF THE LAW. "NO-ONE MUST EXPRESS AFFECTION FOR ANOTHER PERSON WITHOUT FIRST CONSULTING THE MARRIAGE ARRANGEMENT COUNCIL."
BUT IT'S POINTLESS MY DOING THAT. YOU'RE AN ALPHA-GRADED PERSON — YOU CAN'T MARRY A GAMMA LIKE ME . . .
BE STRONG, JANN. PERHAPS SOMETHING WILL HAPPEN TO CHANGE THINGS . . .
And they did — but not for the better.
TRINA — GOOD NEWS, VERY GOOD NEWS! YOU ARE TO BE MARRIED NEXT WEEK!
I-I AM? BUT, FATHER . . .

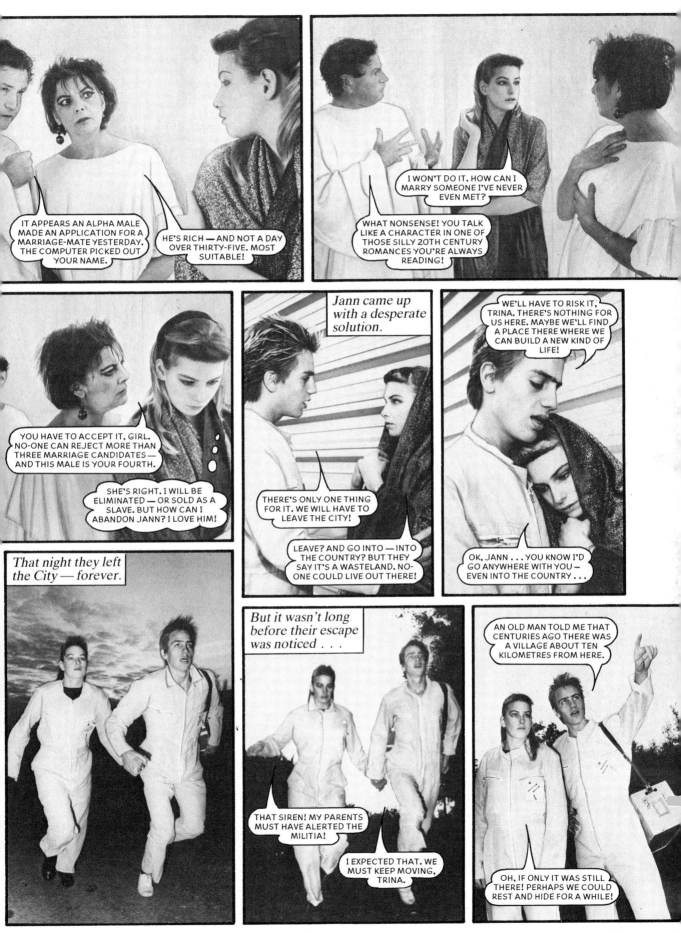

81

You don't need to be a great knit to make these easy sweaters — just start from Square One and get knitting!

MEASUREMENTS: Small [medium, large]; actual bust/chest 108[114,120]cm; length 70[74,78]cm; sleeve seam 45[48,51]cm.
YARN: Of Patons Solo Chunky, 50 g. balls, 7[8,9] in main colour (A); 6[7,7] in contrast (C); 6[6,7] in collar and cuff colour (B).
NEEDLES: A pair each of 5.5 mm. and 6 mm.
TENSION: 15 sts. and 19 rows to 10 cm. square, measured over stocking stitch on 6 mm. needles.
ABBREVIATIONS: K=knit; P=purl; st(s)=stitch(es); beg=beginning; st-st=stocking stitch, one row K, one row P; g-st=garter stitch, every row K.

Note: Instructions for larger sizes are in square brackets [ ]; where there is only one set of figures it applies to all sizes.

THE SQUARES

SQUARE 1: Make 43
Small size:
With 6 mm. needles and A cast on 18 sts. and work 6 rows st-st., beg. with a K row.
* (with B work 2 rows g-st.
With A work 4 rows st-st., beg. with a K row.)
Repeat from (to) once more.
With B work 2 rows g-st. *
With A work 6 rows st-st., beg. with a K row.
Cast off.

Medium size:
With 6 mm. needles and A cast on 19 sts. and work 6 rows st-st., beg. with a K row.
Repeat as for small size from * to *.
With A work 7 rows st-st., beg. with a K row.
Cast off.

Large size:
With 6 mm. needles and A cast on 20 sts. and work 7 rows st-st., beg. with a P row.
Repeat as for small size from * to *.
With A work 7 rows st-st., beg. with a K row.
Cast off.

SQUARE 2: Make 43
As square 1, using C instead of A, and A instead of B.

UNDERARM GUSSETS: Make 2

With 6 mm. needles and B cast on 34[36,38]sts. and work 40[42,44] rows st-st., beg. with a K row.
Cast off.

MAKING UP, COLLAR AND CUFFS

Darn in ends of yarn. Following diagram, sew squares together.
With right side of work facing, 5.5 mm. needles and B, K up 70[76,82]sts. from base of sweater and work 9 rows K2, P2 rib.
Cast off in rib.
With right side of work facing, 5.5 mm. needles and B, K up 38[42,46]sts. from wrist hems and work 9 rows K2, P2 rib.
Cast off in rib.
With right side of work facing, 5.5 mm. needles and B, K up 50[52,54]sts. from base of neck opening and work 139[147,155] rows K2, P2 rib.
Cast off in rib.
Sew collar to neck opening, overlapping base.
Join side, gusset, and sleeve seams.

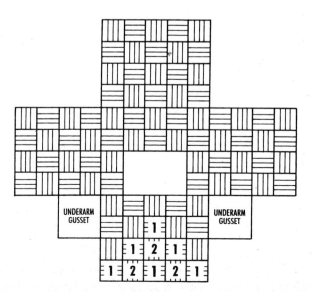

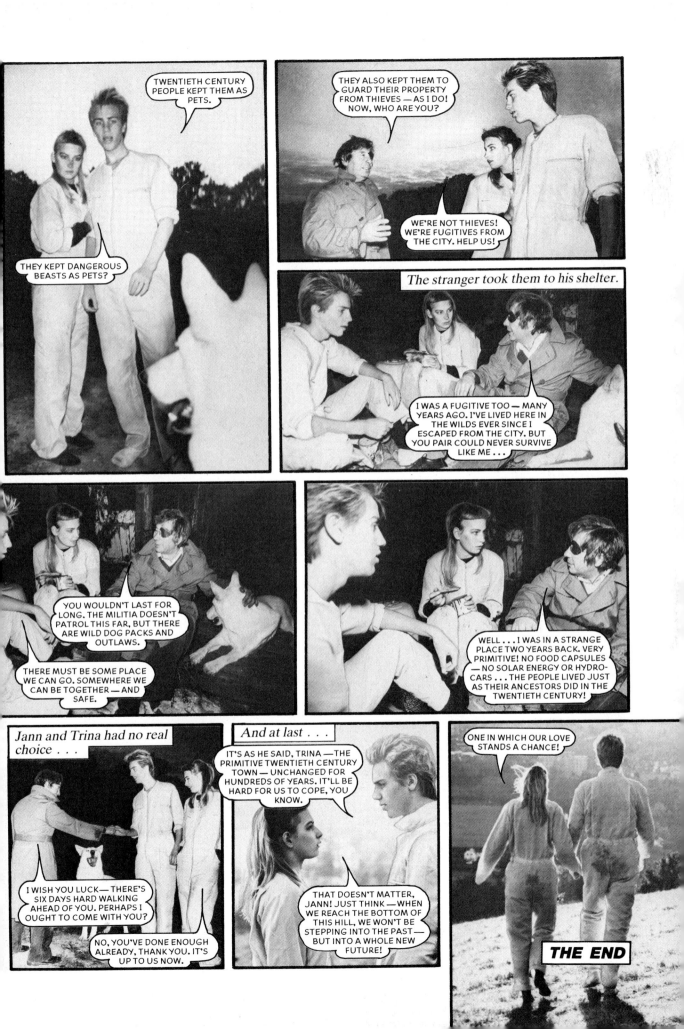

SEEING RED

86

Let's face it, no matter how often you tidy your bedroom, you can guarantee that, two or three days later, it'll once again be looking like its old self — a pig pen!

But things needn't be so messy, and just to prove it, we've come up with a few tidy ideas for storing everything from magazines to make-up brushes — using everything from a lobster pot to a milk crate . . .

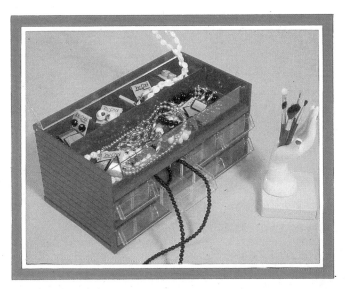

1. Groom Brush Tray — Lifestyle (Arnotts) — **£2.50**
Milk Crate — Tesco — **£2.99**
Plastic Fruit Bowl — Tesco — **75p**
Magazine Holder — John Menzies — **£2.10**
2. Compartment Tool Box — Most D.I.Y. shops — **£4.50**
'Handy' make-up brush holder — Most Dept. Stores — Approx. **£3.99**.
3. Red Stiletto — Compleat Cookshop — **£1.65**
Ornamental Lady — Compleat Cookshop — **£2.49**
4. Straw Basket — Compleat Cookshop — **£1.65**
Lobster Pot — Compleat Cookshop — **£2.49**
Bracelet and Ring Holder — Lifestyle (Arnotts) — **£15.99**

All prices approximate.

Deep down, I knew he'd never see me as anything other than the kid next door, but there was no harm in dreaming.

THE FIRST CUT IS TH

I WATCHED from my bedroom room window as the once-bright convoy of lorries and trailers rumbled along the road and turned laboriously on to the patch of wasteground opposite my house. A thrill of excitement ran through me. The carnival was back again!

I sighed happily and stared out the window. The return of the carnival meant mainly one thing to me — that Patrick would be coming back with them. Not that I had a snowball's chance among all his female fans; but it would be nice to have him around again anyway.

Patrick had lived next door to me for as long as I could remember, until his sixteenth birthday, two years ago when he left with the carnival, that was. I'd always been secretly in love with him, and who wouldn't be! He was tall and broad, with black-brown hair and brown eyes, and a really beautiful smile. But because he was nearly three years older than me and didn't have any sisters for me to be friendly with, I hadn't really had all that much contact with him in all the years we'd known each other.

But just about the time when I thought I might try to do something about it, Patrick had left school and taken off with the carnival. Deep down I knew that he could never see me as anything other than the kid next door; but there was no harm in dreaming, was there?

So that's what I had to do — and, every time he passed me with a new girlfriend, I pretended it was me he had his arm around, me he was walking home, and me he kissed goodnight.

That was the best part — the goodnight kiss. Because though I'd never admit it to my friends, I've never actually had a real kiss. I'd been out with one or two boys in my class at school, but I'd always managed to avoid the awkward

moment. I mean, I wanted to experience a real kiss; of course I did. But not like the sort I knew I'd end up getting; all clashing teeth and not knowing where to put your nose . . . I wanted my first kiss to be something special, something I'd always remember, no matter how many boyfriends I had.

The carnival came to our town every summer, and the showboys — Patrick, Danny, Tommy and Brian — all had their own little fan club, and as Mr and Mrs White, the carnival owners, well knew, the boys were good for business. Patrick, Tom and Danny worked on the Waltzer, and there were always crowds of girls swarming all over the boardwalks, trying to attract their attention. The boys knew what they were doing, too. They said all the right things, teased them, flirted with them and raked in the money.

The night the fair opened, I went over to meet my friends up on the Waltzer. Patrick was in the box beside Billy, who owned the machine.

"I reckon I've got about as much chance with Patrick as you have!"

"Come on, girls, jump on for a fast ride tonight! It's speed, music and thrills, you'll like it girls, you'll like it tonight!"

I laughed to myself as the girls fell over themselves to find a free car. There was no doubt about it, these boys were natural charmers. I smiled as I thought of all the girls, who, like

DEEPEST

me, must have dreamed of being kissed by one or the other of them.

"How's that gorgeous neighbour of yours these days?" asked Caroline, the next day at school. "Did he come back with the carnival again?"

"Oh yes," I assured her with a grin. "He's back. Looking more fantastic than ever, might I add!"

Caroline smiled dreamily. She'd seen Patrick a few times when he was round at my house, which is on the opposite side of town from school.

"What about Peter?" I reminded her, before she got too involved in her daydream.

"What about him? OK, it's nice to have a boyfriend, but I'm allowed to look at other guys, you know." She laughed. "Don't worry, Jane; I haven't got my eye on him. I reckon I've got about as much chance with Patrick as you have!"

Well thank you, Caroline, thank you very much, I thought as I walked towards my English class. That's just what I needed to hear.

There was a debate on that night after school between our school and a visiting team from the next county, so it was dark by the time I left the building. I decided to walk across the showground on my way home, just to see if the Waltzer was still open, or if anyone was about; anyone being Patrick, in case you hadn't guessed!

As I approached the carnival, I heard someone running behind me, and I turned round.

"Patrick, what . . ."

"Ssh, Jane," he hissed, and looked over his shoulder. "Oh heck, they're still following. Look, down here."

He pulled me down where the grass was longest, and we were completely hidden. Three girls from school hurried past; Kate, Janet and Trisha. I hadn't much time for any of them.

"What's all that about?" I demanded, as soon as the three of

them were out of earshot. Patrick rolled over on his back and began to giggle.

"Oh, I was just fed up with the three of them thinking I was going to marry them or something, so I arranged to meet each of them at the chip shop after we shut. Of course, I had to go along to see their faces when they found out, but they spotted me round the corner." He laughed again. "I thought they were going to kill me."

"No wonder," I told him, laughing too. But then we stopped laughing. His eyes looked almost black in the darkness, and the faint light from the carnival shimmered on the edges of his hair.

Then it happened. The moment I'd dreamed of . . .

"I didn't hurt you when I hauled you down like that, did I?" Patrick asked softly.

Then it happened. The moment I'd dreamed of. He bent over, and I knew he was going to kiss me.

I'll always remember opening my eyes and looking up at him with the sky dark, and the stars twinkling.

"Be happy, Janie," was all he said, and then he was gone.

I walked home slowly, thinking. I'd been right to wait. I could tell by the way Patrick had looked at me that he knew it was my first real kiss and that he understood.

I know I'll never go out with him now. But I'll always be a little in love with Patrick, and I'll always have the memory of my first kiss . . .

Warming up — stand straight with your feet apart, and put your arms above your head. Bend over slowly, and touch the floor. Straighten up, repeat, but this time push your arms through your legs.

THAT BODY

All right, you lot. Hands up who's feeling guilty 'cos they've eaten too much lately? Yes, just as we suspected! But never mind, it's Patches to the rescue as usual! We've worked out a few exercises to help you shed the pounds you've gained, and get back to your sylph-like self!

The bottom line — kneel up with your arms above your head, fingers touching. Keep your body facing forward, and lower your bottom to touch the floor on the right, then swing to the left and down.

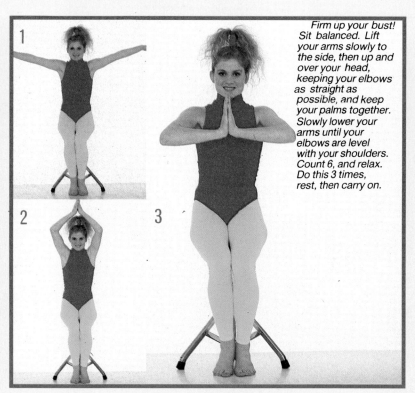

Firm up your bust! Sit balanced. Lift your arms slowly to the side, then up and over your head, keeping your elbows as straight as possible, and keep your palms together. Slowly lower your arms until your elbows are level with your shoulders. Count 6, and relax. Do this 3 times, rest, then carry on.

Waist bend — stand with your feet apart. Put arms above your head and link hands. Keep your arms and body straight, and bend slowly to the right as far as you can. Straighten up and repeat, this time going to the left.

Stomach control — lie flat on your back with your arms above your head. Breathe out, pull yourself up slowly and stretch forward. Breathe in and return.

IT'S OVER..

SADLY, and all too often, what was once the closest and most perfect of relationships splits up — and if you weren't the one who wanted that split to happen, you're left with the distinct impression that the world is a lousy place and that there's not a lot of point in you having any part of it . . .

To begin with, you'll just want to mope around feeling sorry for yourself — which can be dangerous if it goes on too long. Twenty-four hours of sniffing into the hankies is fine, and friends and family will be sympathetic. Months of dragging around being a tragedy queen is exhausting for everybody — including yourself.

So what practical things can you do to help yourself cope?

Can You Handle It?

The first and most important one is to talk it all out with someone close to you — of either sex — whom you can trust to be sympathetic, listen, and not just rabbit on for hours about how he/she always knew the little rat was a little rat. At this juncture you don't really need opinions; you need to get a lot of things out of your system, and chances are that'll include tears, so try not to pour out your soul to someone you'd feel embarrassed crying in front of.

Once you've got over the blotchy-faced, red-eyed bit and can think, do that. Take yourself off somewhere quiet, your own room, the loo, the park, the garden shed — anywhere at all — and consider all the advantages and disadvantages of not seeing him any more. If you're honest, there'll probably be

quite a few more good points than bad! And don't torture yourself by taking the relationship to pieces, wondering if you'd said this or that, things would be different? It's over, and you can't change it, so instead, think about all the things you didn't like about him. You may very well find some of the thoughts that come into your head very surprising indeed — and if they surprise you because you'd never've thought you really didn't like the fact he always called you fish face, then you're moving out a little bit along the way from the initial sheer desperation.

One thing you mustn't ever do, no matter how tempting, is sit down and write a long, soggy letter telling him how he's broken your heart and ruined you for other boys for ever. If he wanted to finish it, then he wanted to finish it, and getting a communication like that will only make him all the more convinced he was right in the first place — and you'll probably die of embarrassment if you ever bump into each other again, and most people do.

If you must pour out your heart on paper (because there isn't anyone else you can talk to, perhaps) then do it — but make yourself the firm promise that next day you'll tear the paper up. And keep that promise to yourself. The last thing you need at the moment is him to be reading out your tear-washed scribbles to all his mates and having a giggle with them at your expense.

Don't, either, promptly chuck everything he ever gave you into the dustbin. Pack it away for a bit. Because in a couple of months when you're madly in love with someone else, you'll probably want something to remind you of the times you had with Rat-fink. Cutting off your nose to spite your face is a natural reaction, and ripping up all his letters and cards (if he

so how do you cope when love breaks down?

ever sent you any) is momentarily very satisfying. It's also stupid! You'll only wish you hadn't later on.

Just Like Starting Over . . .

But the most important way of the lot to cope is also the most difficult — you have to start going out again with your mates. You can't sit in front of "Coronation Street" every night (supposing it was on every night), and there's a limit to how many times you can re-read even the "Patches" annual without getting just a teeny bit bored.

You need people; close friends will know this. They'll suggest you go with them to the disco, or a party, or just out for a coffee — and the more you say you don't feel like it, the less sympathetic they'll become. You have to try to make the effort, and let's face it, you'll have to go out again sooner or later, so the sooner you try to get back into circulation, the better.

Don't panic, though, if on your first outing everything everywhere reminds you of him — and consequently of him and you together. That's only natural if you really cared about him, and in fact it's quite a healthy reaction. Just try not to burst into an entire flood of tears or you'll spend most of the evening retouching your make-up, and your friends will get really cheesed off.

When people you don't know particularly well casually ask you where he is, tell them the truth — that you've split up. No point in saying he's gone on a hang-gliding course if, five minutes later, he walks into the room with another girl on his arm! It's never going to be easy if he does appear when you're least expecting it. You'll simply have to stay there and brazen it out. It was going to happen sooner or later anyhow. He may well ignore you. You may well want to ignore him. And if you can both get away with it without causing unpleasantness, then fair enough. But the last thing you — or anybody else around you — wants or needs right at the moment is a scene, so don't cause one, and if he looks as if he might, walk away and talk to your friends, or excuse yourself, politely, and leave.

Then again, if he does turn up at a gathering you're at, don't spend the entire evening in a huddle in a corner with your best mate telling her how awful he is. That really doesn't accomplish anything. Be as close to your normal party self as you can, but don't flirt outrageously with every other male in sight. That'll just make you look cheap in everybody's eyes, and although revenge can be very sweet indeed, that kind of revenge will simply earn you an unnecessary reputation.

Second Time Around

As far as trusting a second time around is concerned, try to bear in mind that all boys aren't the same, and you will learn to trust somebody else some day. So next time you're asked out, play it by ear and if you fancy the bloke's company, then go! It doesn't necessarily mean it's going to turn into the next "Romeo and Juliet", but why not give it a chance? Locking yourself away from every male in sight because of one bad experience is pretty senseless, even though it's a natural reaction at the time.

But there's another side to that coin, too — which is don't just accept dates willy-nilly with boys you don't fancy in an attempt to "get over him". You won't enjoy it, they won't enjoy it, and you'll just end up missing the Rat-fink more than ever.

Coping with the end of a relationship is difficult. No-one would pretend it isn't. But provided you can try to be sensible, and provided you can eventually resurrect your sense of humour again, it is possible. It just takes time. There's no-one that you can't get over eventually.

And once you've realised that, you're already halfway there.

...AND

"Neil looks great now! His hair's lovely, and it's really nice to see him wearing decent clothes instead of those flaming jeans! You've certainly put a stop to our arguments!"

Thanks to Stevin, Maureen and everyone at the Rainbow Room for their help.